UNIT 2

WHY ARE THERE SEASONS?

UNIT 2
Why Are There Seasons?

In this unit, students are systematically guided toward an understanding of what causes our planet's seasons. Many students and adults have misconceptions about the causes of seasons. We often need to reflect on and discard some of our old, familiar concepts about the Sun-Earth relationship before we can understand the actual reasons behind the seasons. The process of using evidence to revise models or explanations is at the heart of science, and in this unit, students constantly challenge and revise their own ideas in the same way scientists do.

Many of us hold onto and even embellish erroneous personal explanations for the seasons throughout our school years, and we become very good at fitting new information into our old, comfortable private models. Our students often do the same. They arrive in class with their own frameworks and preconceptions (also called alternative conceptions).

Research done by Dr. Philip M. Sadler at the Harvard-Smithsonian Center for Astrophysics found that understanding the causes of seasons is challenging for people of all ages. The now-famous video, *A Private Universe*, which was one result of Dr. Sadler's research, shows that even Harvard University graduates and faculty are hard-pressed to correctly answer the question, "What causes the seasons?" They may think they know and speak confidently, but most of them hold mistaken ideas. Many of them state that the changing Earth-Sun distance causes the seasons. They mistakenly believe that summer occurs when the Earth is closer to the Sun, and that winter occurs when the Earth is farther from the Sun. They hold this view despite a knowledge of the following facts:

- Earth is a sphere.
- Earth spins once every 24 hours, giving rise to day and night.
- Earth spins with a tilt.
- Earth orbits the Sun once a year.

These facts are prerequisites to understanding what causes seasons, but a full understanding requires a synthesis of these facts using data, models, discourse, and actual experience. (*A Private Universe* can be purchased on DVD or viewed free at http://www.learner.org/resources/series28.html or https://www.cfa.harvard.edu/pcgi/conf_reg/smgorder.pl Educators can obtain a free copy of the DVD. For ordering information, see the Resources and References section on page 59.

If it's not distance, what DOES cause the seasons?

The Earth spins about an imaginary line called the axis of rotation, or north-south axis. The spin of this axis is tilted so that the North Pole always points toward the North Star. As the Earth revolves around the Sun, the Northern Hemisphere is tilted toward the Sun around the time of the summer solstice in June and away from the Sun around the time of the winter solstice in December.

Credit: NASA/NSSDC

When the Northern Hemisphere is tilted toward the Sun, it is summer because there are more hours of daylight, and sunlight strikes the Northern Hemisphere at a higher angle (more perpendicular), making the sunlight more intense on the ground, which results in an increase in heat.

No single experience is likely to move your students from their initial conceptions to a full and accurate understanding. Such understanding takes time and multiple experiences. Research indicates that one of the best ways to help people correct their misconceptions is to provide them with revealing experiences and allow them time to compare and discuss alternative explanations. In this way, they can discover the flaws in their own thinking and construct more accurate explanations. Providing such experiences and the time for reflection upon them is precisely what this unit seeks to do.

UNIT 2
Why Are There Seasons?

SESSION SUMMARIES (7 Sessions)

2.1 Introducing Seasons and the Pre-unit 2 Questionnaire

In this session, students are asked to brainstorm seasonal changes that they've experienced or observed. They complete the Pre-unit 2 Questionnaire and then discuss the questions together, explaining their reasoning and ideas. Preconceptions and disparities in answers are noted, but correct answers are not yet revealed. Then students draw a model of the Sun-Earth system on the scale of a football field, discover that Earth's orbit is nearly circular, and that the distance between the Sun and Earth varies only a tiny amount during the year. During this session, the key concepts added to the classroom concept wall are:
- *Scientists use models to demonstrate ideas, explain observations, and make predictions.*
- *Earth travels around the Sun in a nearly circular orbit.*
- *The Sun is very close to the center of Earth's orbit.*

2.2 Does Variation in the Sun-Earth Distance Cause Seasons?

In this session, the class analyzes year-long temperature graphs for different locations around the world. They discover that the pattern of temperature change from summer to winter in one hemisphere is reversed with respect to the opposite hemisphere—further evidence that the Sun-Earth distance is not responsible for seasons. Next, the class observes another scale model of the Sun-Earth system and concludes that the Sun-Earth distance is enormous compared with the size of Earth, a fact that will help students to understand that Earth's tilt does not make a significant difference in its distance to the Sun. The session concludes with students in evidence circles discussing the question, "Do changes in the Sun–Earth distance cause the seasons?" They use what they have learned so far to support their answers. During this session, the key concepts added to the classroom concept wall are:
- *Patterns of average-temperature change (and seasons) are opposite for the Northern and Southern Hemispheres.*
- *Earth's tilt does not significantly change its distance from the Sun.*
- *Scientific explanations are based on evidence gathered from observations and investigations.*

2.3 Hours of Daylight and Seasons

In this session, students share their findings from last session's evidence circles. Teams then graph the number of daylight hours, month by month, for cities at different latitudes. This reveals a symmetrical pattern of daylight hours that is opposite for the Northern and Southern Hemispheres. Students discover some months when the Sun never sets and some months when the Sun never rises in regions near the poles, such as Alaska and Antarctica. They also learn about the terms *equinox* and *solstice*. The graphing and data-analysis activities in this session lay the groundwork for the modeling of seasons in Session 2.4. During this session, the key concepts added to the classroom concept wall are:
- *For any given latitude, spring and summer days have more hours of daylight, and fall and winter nights are longer.*
- *In the Northern and Southern Hemispheres, day-length changes (and seasons) are opposite one another during the year.*
- *Day-length changes are more dramatic farther away from the Equator.*

2.4 Observing Seasons

In this session, the class models seasons. They first compare two Earth models: one with no tilt and one with a tilted spin axis. Students stand in a large circle around a light-bulb Sun with their model Earths and discover how the tilt of Earth's spin axis toward the North Star causes seasons. This model is especially effective in showing what causes seasonal variations in day length. Afterward, students discuss, answer, and write responses to questions about what they have learned. This written work can serve as an assessment of student understanding up to this point in the unit. During this session, the key concept added to the classroom concept wall is:

• *Earth's tilted spin axis causes seasonal changes in hours of daylight and night throughout the year.*

2.5 Intensity of Sunlight

In this session, students extend the model from the previous session to explore how Earth's tilt causes sunlight to hit the ground at different angles in different seasons and how this changes the intensity of the sunlight on the surface of Earth. At the start of winter (the winter solstice), rays of sunlight strike the ground at a shallow angle and are less intense on the ground than the steeper, more perpendicular, rays of sunlight when summer begins (at the summer solstice). Students work in teams to measure and record the intensity of "sunlight" (from a light-bulb Sun in the center of the room) at different locations on Earth globes during different seasons. They use this data in a closing discussion about how light intensity relates to seasons. This evidence rounds out students' understanding of the real reasons for seasons. During this session, the key concepts added to the classroom concept wall are:

• *At the beginning of summer, sunlight falls at a steep angle and shines most intensely on Earth's surface.*
• *At the beginning of winter, sunlight falls at a shallow angle and shines least intensely on Earth's surface.*

2.6 The Reasons for Seasons

In this session, equipped with understandings gained from all their investigations in this unit, students again work in evidence circles to use their newly acquired knowledge to debate three explanations for the seasons. This last session gives students an opportunity to internalize and deepen their new understanding of what causes the seasons: that Earth is a spinning globe whose axis tilts with respect to its orbit around the Sun, and that this axial tilt gives rise to: (a) a varying number of daylight hours in different seasons, and (b) variations in the intensity of sunlight on the ground related to the angle at which the light strikes the ground. There are no new key concepts for this session.

Optional: Prerequisite Activities

In this optional session, three activities can be used, depending on the needs of your class, to strengthen your students' understanding of (1) the shape of Earth, (2) how the spinning of Earth causes day and night, and (3) the shape of Earth's orbit. The first two activities are best presented before beginning Unit 2, while the third is a hands-on activity about ellipses that deepens and extends concepts introduced in Session 2.2. These activities reinforce foundational ideas, without which students cannot build an accurate understanding of what causes the seasons.

SESSION 2.1
Introducing Seasons and the Pre-unit 2 Questionnaire

Before beginning this unit with your students, it is necessary that they have some fundamental knowledge about Earth—its shape and movement. Please see page 271 for more details.

Unit Goals

The seasons are not caused by variations in Earth's distance from the Sun.

Earth's spin axis remains tilted toward Polaris as it orbits the Sun.

Earth's tilt does not significantly change its distance from the Sun.

Seasons are caused by Earth's tilt, which affects the intensity of sunlight and the number of daylight hours at different locations on Earth.

Overview

There are many misconceptions about what causes the seasons—a common one is that the seasons are caused by variation in the distance of Earth from the Sun. Many believe that as Earth moves in its orbit, its distance from the Sun changes greatly throughout the year. In reality, although Earth's orbit is an ellipse, it is a very nearly circular ellipse, and the variation in its distance to the Sun is minimal. In this session, students are asked to recall seasonal changes that they've experienced or observed. They complete the Pre-unit 2 Questionnaire then discuss the questions together, explaining their reasoning and ideas. Preconceptions and disparities in answers are noted, but **correct answers are not yet revealed.** Then students draw a model of the Sun-Earth system on the scale of a football field, discover that Earth's orbit is nearly circular, and that the distance between the Sun and Earth varies only a tiny amount during the year. During this session, the key concepts added to the classroom concept wall are:

- *Scientists use models to demonstrate ideas, explain observations, and make predictions.*
- *Earth travels around the Sun in a nearly circular orbit.*
- *The Sun is very close to the center of Earth's orbit.*

Introducing Seasons and the Pre-unit 2 Questionnaire	Estimated Time
Thinking About Seasonal Changes	5 minutes
Taking the Pre-unit 2 Questionnaire	15 minutes
Discussing Questionnaire Responses	10 minutes
Football-Field Model of the Sun-Earth System	15 minutes
Total	**45 minutes**

What You Need

For the class:
- ❑ overhead projector or computer with large-screen monitor or LCD projector
- ❑ prepared key concept sheets from the copymaster packet or CD-ROM file
- ❑ two sentence strips
- ❑ a marker
- ❑ a chalkboard OR overhead projector OR sheet of butcher paper
- ❑ transparencies of the Pre-unit 2 Questionnaire (four pages) from the transparency packet or CD-ROM file
- ❑ transparency of Distances from Earth to Sun from the transparency packet or CD-ROM file
- ❑ a scale-model car (or any other scale model)
- ❑ 1 large, round embroidery hoop or hula hoop (optional for this session, but is used in Session 2.2)

TEACHER CONSIDERATIONS

TEACHING NOTES

A note about time management for this session. To save time, a Football-Field Model Template has been provided as an option for you to use with students. The Seasonal Changes chart is also optional, and the hula-hoop model can be done at the beginning of Session 2.2.

ASSESSMENT OPPORTUNITY
CRITICAL JUNCTURE: NECESSARY PREREQUISITE CONCEPTS

Before starting Unit 2 with your students, it is necessary that they know the following:

- Earth is a sphere.
- Earth spins once every 24 hours, giving rise to day and night.
- Earth spins with a tilt.
- Earth orbits the Sun once a year.

If your students need review of these fundamental and key concepts, we strongly recommend that you allow extra class time to present the prerequisite activities: Shape-of-Earth Survey (page 368) and Night and Day on Mount Nose (page 370).

After completing these activities, consider adding these prerequisite key concepts to the classroom concept wall for your students' reference throughout the unit.

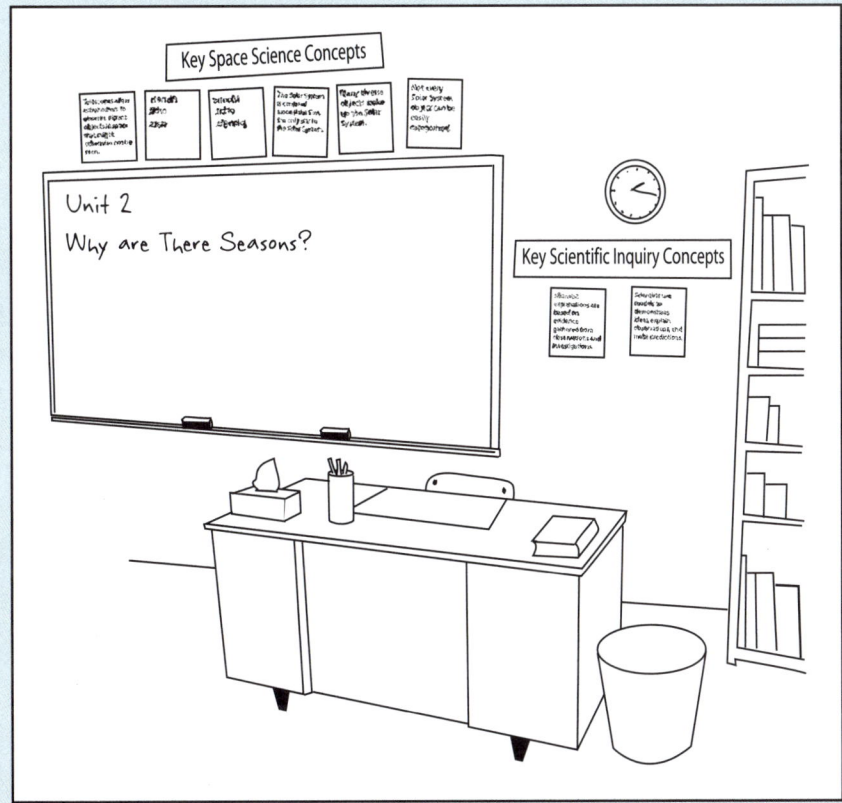

Key Vocabulary

Scientific Inquiry Vocabulary

Evidence
Model
Observationa
Prediction
Scale
Scale model
Scientific explanation

Space Science Vocabulary

Equator
Equinox
Hemisphere
Intensity
Latitude
Orbit
Solstice
Spin axis

UNIT 2 • 267

SESSION 2.1 Introducing Seasons and the Pre-unit 2 Questionnaire

For each student:
- ❑ 1 copy of the Pre-unit 2 Questionnaire (four pages) from the copymaster packet or CD-ROM file
- ❑ a sheet of paper *OR* 1 copy of the Football-Field Model Template student sheet from the copymaster packet or CD-ROM file
- ❑ 1 file folder

Getting Ready

1. **Arrange for the appropriate projector format to display images to the class.** Decide whether you will be using the overheads or the CD-ROM. Set up an overhead projector or a computer with a large-screen monitor or LCD projector.

2. **Designate a wall or bulletin board in the classroom as the unit's concept wall.** Use the concept wall as a space to post the key concepts for each session in this unit. It is helpful to distinguish between the two categories of key concepts—Space Science and Scientific Inquiry. See page 267 for an example of a concept wall. Although the concept wall does take up a fair amount of space, it is a very useful and important learning tool for your students.

3. **Prepare the key concept sheets.** Make a copy of each key concept and have them ready to post onto the classroom concept wall during the session.

4. **Prepare the concept wall headings.** Using the sentence strips and marker, make the two headings for the concept wall—one labeled Key Space Science Concepts and the other labeled Key Scientific Inquiry Concepts.

5. **Decide whether to create and post a Seasonal Changes chart.** Read through the Thinking About Seasonal Changes opening activity and decide whether you plan to create a Seasonal Changes chart. If so, use a sheet of butcher paper to make the chart during class. Also decide whether or not you would like to keep the chart posted.

6. **Copy the Pre-unit 2 Questionnaire.** Make a copy of the questionnaire (four pages) for each student.

TEACHER CONSIDERATIONS

TEACHING NOTES

The key concepts can be posted in many different ways. If you don't want to use sentence sheets, here are some alternatives:

- Write the key concepts out on sentence strips.
- Write the key concepts out before class on a posted piece of butcher paper. Cover each concept with a strip of butcher paper and reveal each one as it is brought up in the class discussion.

Some teachers have also made a Word Wall during the unit—a list of new words (as they arise) with brief definitions, such as *latitude* and *longitude*, *solstice* and *equinox*, and any other terms students may be encountering for the first time.

Although saving and posting the Seasonal Changes chart is optional, students may enjoy referring to it throughout the unit.

SESSION 2.1 Introducing Seasons and the Pre-unit 2 Questionnaire

7. **Decide if students will draw their own football fields.** If you are short on class time, an alternative would be to copy the Football-Field Model Template for your students to use.

8. **Decide if you will present any of the optional prerequisite activities: Shape-of-Earth Survey and/or Night and Day on Mount Nose.** Students should have some fundamental understandings in place before you begin this unit. Both of these optional activities can be used to review necessary concepts. See page 267 for more about these activities and for the necessary prerequisite student concepts.

GO! Thinking About Seasonal Changes

1. **Discussing seasonal changes.** Tell the class that in this unit they will be learning about what causes Earth's seasons. Begin a class discussion about seasonal changes by asking students, "What kinds of changes have you noticed taking place during different seasons?" [It gets darker earlier, the weather gets hotter, flowers bloom, baseball season opens, it snows, etc.] Accept a wide variety of responses, jotting ideas down on the chalkboard, overhead projector, or on a piece of butcher paper. Be sure to leave some space for creating a Seasonal Changes chart, if you plan to make one. (See Step #3.)

2. **Categorizing seasonal changes.** Tell the class that these seasonal changes can be organized into general categories. Based on what students have listed, point out the categories or, if time permits, have the class brainstorm possible categories themselves. Some examples of possible general categories include *biological changes* (plants blooming or animals hibernating), *meteorological changes* (falling snow; rainy weather; long, hot days) and *sociological changes* (dressing up for Halloween; the start of baseball season; going holiday shopping; putting on coats, hats, and scarves).

TEACHER CONSIDERATIONS

PROVIDING MORE EXPERIENCE
Optional: Shape-of-Earth Survey. If you think your class needs to review the concept that Earth's shape is spherical, please see the activity in the optional session on page 368 at the end of this unit.

Optional: Night and Day on Mount Nose. Similarly, if you think your class needs to review the concept that day and night are caused by the spinning of Earth, please see the activity in the Optional session on page 370 at the end of this unit.

TEACHING NOTES
Students really enjoy discussing seasonal changes, but this opening discussion could be shortened or omitted if class time is limited. Alternatively, if you have additional time, a complementary activity, Name the Season, can be found in the GEMS guide *The Real Reasons for Seasons*.

The seasonal-change categories suggested may not be relevant for the ideas your students will generate. Use their list of seasonal changes to come up with more appropriate category titles such as life, weather, holidays, sports events, school events, etc.

SESSION 2.1 Introducing Seasons and the Pre-unit 2 Questionnaire

3. **Optional: Create a Seasonal Changes chart.** On the chalkboard, overhead projector, or on a piece of butcher paper, create a chart for categorizing the seasonal changes. Draw lines to create rows and columns, then list the four seasons vertically along the left edge of the chart and write the category names horizontally across the top of the chart. Have students help you categorize the changes they've listed into the appropriate spots on the chart. Elicit additional events and changes typical of each season until there are at least a few examples listed for each cell in the chart.

	Weather	Life	School Events
Fall			
Winter			
Spring			
Summer			

4. **Learning about what causes the seasons.** Say that all of the seasonal changes listed in the chart are examples of how people observe the passing of different seasons every year. Tell students that this unit will help them better understand why we experience four different seasons.

Taking the Pre-unit 2 Questionnaire

1. **Introduce the Pre-unit 2 Questionnaire.** Tell the class that they are now going to fill out a questionnaire about what they think causes the seasons. Emphasize that the questionnaire **will not be graded**. Instead, it is to get students thinking about what they know about seasons and why seasons happen. Say that it's okay for them to be unsure about the answers to some of the questions. Later, near the end of the unit, after students learn more about seasons and what causes them, they will take the questionnaire again to see how their ideas have changed.

2. **Many people don't know why seasons occur.** Explain that most people, including adults, don't really understand why there are seasons. Say that even a group of Harvard University graduates who were asked to explain the seasons had mistaken ideas. Tell students that after this unit, they will understand what causes the seasons—and know more about this topic than most people!

One teacher said, "Having the questionnaires really opened my eyes to what my students know and don't know. There are HUGE misconceptions about the seasons and I can't wait to see my students figure out the 'real' reasons for the seasons."

TEACHER CONSIDERATIONS

TEACHING NOTES

Creating a Seasonal Changes chart is optional. To save time, if you prefer, just have a class discussion about seasonal changes.

Name:

Pre-unit 2 Questionnaire: Why Are There Seasons? (continued)

...ink it is hotter in the United States in June than in December?
...swers that are correct.

...Sun itself gives off more heat and energy in June and less in December.

...th is closer to the Sun in June and farther away from the Sun in

...United States is closer to the Sun in June and farther from the Sun in

...United States is tilted more toward the Sun in June and away from the ...mber.

...Sun appears higher in the sky in June, and its rays are more intense.

...he United States, there are more hours of daylight in June than in

...th drawing, which picture of Earth best shows its size and distance from ... the best answer.

A. Earth

B. Earth

C. Earth is three page lengths away and too small to be seen on the paper.

Name:

Pre-unit 2 Questionnaire: Why Are There Seasons?

1. When Earth is closest to the Sun, which of the following is true? **Circle the best answer.**
   A. It is winter everywhere on Earth.
   B. It is summer everywhere on Earth.
   C. Earth's distance to the Sun causes summer in the Northern Hemisphere.
   D. Earth's distance to the Sun has nothing to do with the reasons for seasons.

2. Which of the drawings do you think best shows the shape of Earth's orbit around the Sun? (This is a top-down view.) **Circle the best answer.**
   A. B. C. D.

Name:

Pre-unit 2 Questionnaire: Why Are There Seasons? (continued)

...ere are two Earths. One Earth is where our Earth is. The other Earth is ...er to the Sun. Which place on these two Earths would be hotter—point A ... answer.

A

B

Sun's rays

...swer.

Name:

Pre-unit 2 Questionnaire: Why Are There Seasons? (continued)

5. These two pictures show the same tree on two different days at noon. Why do the Sun's rays come in at different angles? **Explain why this occurs.**

A SUN

B SUN

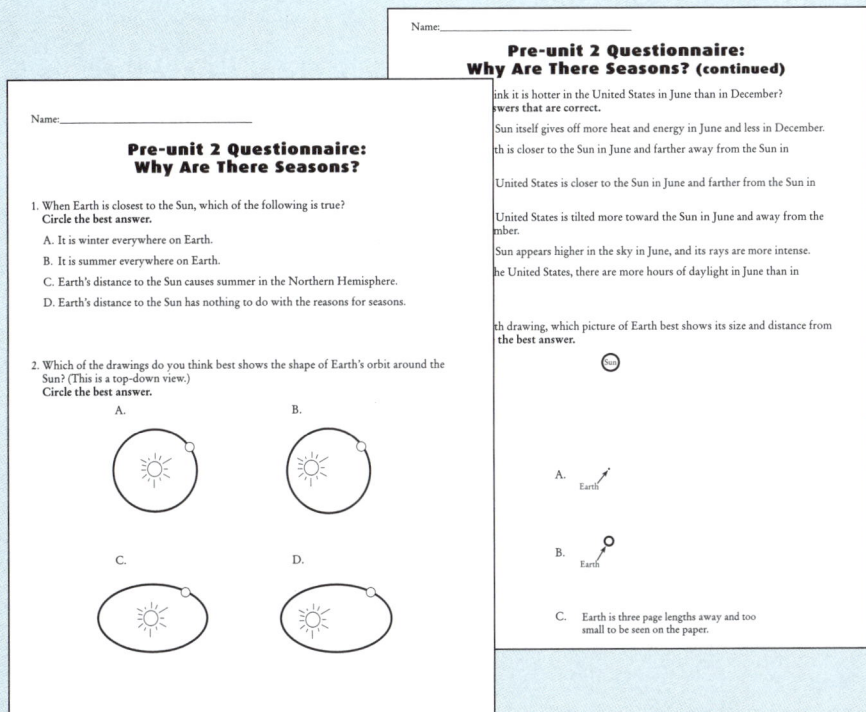

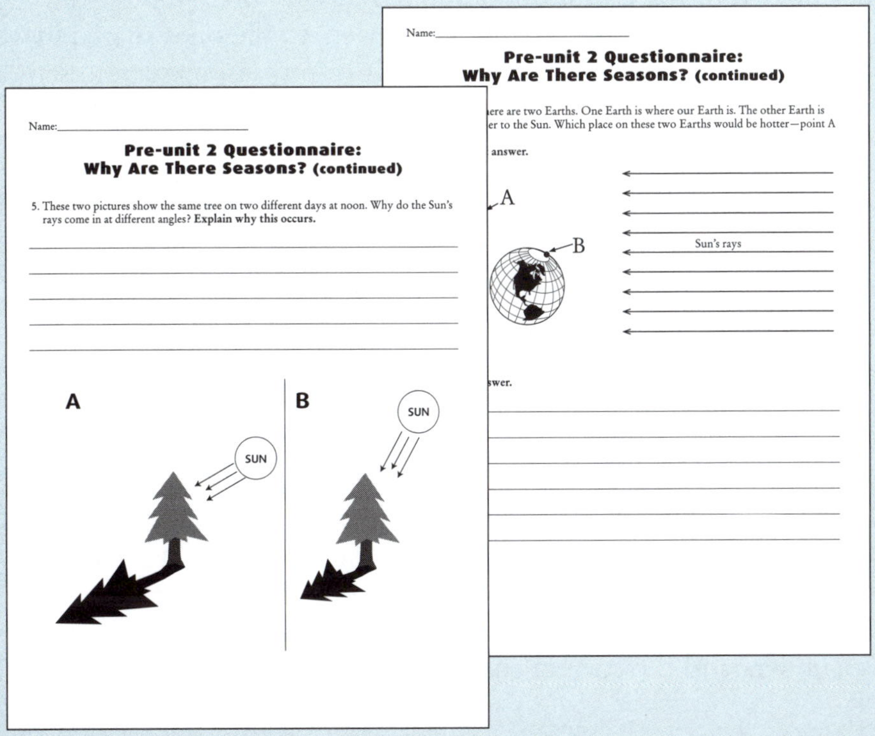

SESSION 2.1 Introducing Seasons and the Pre-unit 2 Questionnaire

3. **Instructions for questionnaire.** Tell students they should do their own work on the questionnaire, without talking to one another. They should try to answer the questions as best as they can. Explain that if they don't know the answer to a question, a careful guess is okay—but they should be prepared to explain why they answered the questions the way they did.

4. **Pass out questionnaires and have students begin.** Give the class a few minutes of advance warning before collecting the questionnaires.

Discussing Questionnaire Responses

1. **Students discuss responses.** Say that students will now have a chance to discuss their responses to the questionnaire. Show the transparency of the Pre-unit 2 Questionnaire.

2. **Refrain from revealing correct responses.** While students will be curious to know if they have answered the questions correctly, *do not reveal the correct responses to the questionnaire during this discussion.* Instead, say that students will find out the answers to these and other questions about seasons as they learn more in this unit. Explain that the purpose of this initial discussion is to give everyone an opportunity to share what they think causes the seasons. All ideas are valid for discussion!

3. **Encourage class discussion.** Have a few volunteers share what they answered for Question #1 and *why*. Ask other students if they agree with or have alternative answers to the ones shared by their classmates. As students share their responses, tease out their reasoning by asking them follow-up questions such as, "Would you explain your reasoning?" or "How did you arrive at your answer?" Proceed through each of the questions on the questionnaire in this way, allowing for as many students as possible to share their thoughts.

4. **Invite students to share any additional ideas.** Students may have other ideas not addressed or raised by the questionnaire. Ask, "Does anyone have any other ideas to share with the class about what causes seasons?" Accept all ideas students bring up.

5. **The correct answers aren't important right now.** Explain to the class that you aren't going to tell them the answers that scientists would consider correct, because you want them to continue to think about these questions. Upcoming activities will help them discover and understand the correct answers for themselves.

TEACHER CONSIDERATIONS

PROVIDING MORE EXPERIENCE
Students take the questionnaire home. Tell students they will each receive a copy of the Pre-unit 2 Questionnaire to take home for use with a friend or family member. Students should tell their questionnaire "subjects" that they are about to begin a unit about what causes seasons, and that they are gathering data about what a sample of other people think. Students can tell their subjects that their responses will be anonymous, and they shouldn't feel embarrassed if they aren't sure of the answers, because that's very common. Hand out one (or two) blank questionnaires to each student. Ask them to bring in the completed questionnaires by the next class session.

Optional: Provide time for students to tally answers and make a graph to represent the responses of friends and family.

ABOUT THE PRE-UNIT 2 QUESTIONNAIRE RESPONSES
Refrain from revealing the correct answers to students! Do not give out the correct answers immediately after students have taken the Pre-unit 2 Questionnaire. Even better—do not give out the correct answers at all! Students will discover the answers themselves throughout the subsequent sessions in this unit. Research demonstrates such self-discovery and the process of reflecting on and grappling with alternative conceptions is crucial for helping students achieve enduring understanding. Without it, many students are likely to fall back on their prior mistaken ideas.

The correct responses to the questionnaire are given here *for your reference only.* These are only brief discussions of responses. As the unit proceeds, additional, more detailed evidence for and understanding of each of these questions is presented. There is also some information here that can help you interpret what various student responses may indicate about their thinking. Because many students may have guessed a correct answer, discussion of the rationale behind their responses is necessary and valuable in bringing out and understanding their thinking.

1. When Earth is closest to the Sun, which of the following is true? (The correct answer is D.)

Ironically, Earth is closest to the Sun around January 4th—which is winter in the Northern Hemisphere! The distance to the Sun has nothing to do with the causes of the seasons. Students who firmly believe that distance does make a difference are very likely to choose answer B, since it *seems* logical that it would be summer everywhere on Earth when Earth is closest to the Sun.

continued on page 277

SESSION 2.1 Introducing Seasons and the Pre-unit 2 Questionnaire

If your students are not familiar with the dimensions of a football field, you may need to take a little time to explain.

Football-Field Model of the Sun-Earth System

1. **Does a changing Sun-Earth distance cause the seasons?** If any students mentioned that the seasons are caused by the changing distance between the Sun and Earth as Earth orbits the Sun, say that the class will now do an activity to investigate if this might be true. Tell the class that one way to get an accurate sense of the distance between Earth and the Sun is by constructing a *scale model* of the Sun-Earth system.

2. **Introduce the concept wall.** Point out the space in the classroom you've designated for the concept wall. Explain that as the class learns important or key concepts about the seasons, the concept wall will help them to keep track of what they've learned.

3. **Introduce (or review) models and scale models.** (If your students are familiar with both of these, briefly review the following discussion points with them.) Say that a model is not the real thing, but it shows something about the real thing accurately—such as what it looks like or how it moves. Explain that scientists frequently use models to study or understand something that may be difficult for them to observe directly. Next, hold up the scale-model car and explain that not only is the toy car a model, it is also built to scale—meaning that someone measured every part of a real car and made each part smaller by the same factor to construct a scale model of the car. Post on the concept wall, under Key Scientific Inquiry Concepts:

   Scientists use models to demonstrate ideas, explain observations, and make predictions.

4. **Use a football field scale model to visualize Sun-Earth distance.** Tell students they will be making scale models of the Sun-Earth system by using a drawing of a football field. Explain that their football-field diagrams will help them visualize the scaled distances between Earth and the Sun. They will use their scale models to investigate whether changes in Earth's distance from the Sun are responsible for the seasons.

5. **Pass out sheet of paper and pencil to each student.** Have students title their sheet of paper, "Football-Field Model of the Sun-Earth System." Say that you will show them how to draw their football fields. (If you've opted to copy the Football-Field Model Template for your students, pass these out, skip Step #6, and go on to Step #7.)

6. **Show students how to draw the football-field model.** Using the chalkboard or overhead projector, show students how to draw their football fields. Have them follow along as you go through the steps below. (This model can be roughly sketched without using a ruler.)

One teacher said, "Students were excited about what they learned about the shape of Earth's orbit. Later in the unit, all I would have to say is, 'Remember the football field?' and they could visualize the correct shape of Earth's orbit."

TEACHER CONSIDERATIONS

ABOUT THE PRE-UNIT 2 QUESTIONNAIRE RESPONSES
continued from page 275

2. Which of the drawings do you think best shows the shape of Earth's orbit around the Sun? (The correct answer is A.)

Although many people have heard or learned that Earth's orbit is elliptical, in reality it is nearly circular and only *slightly* elliptical. Students who choose answers B, C, or D may believe that the seasons are caused by variations in Earth's proximity to the Sun—a very common misconception. This misconception that Earth's orbit is highly elliptical is fostered by the many illustrations in books and posters that show Earth's orbit drawn from the side, as though viewed from an oblique angle, rather than a top-down view.

3. Why do you think it is hotter in the United States in June than in December? (Answers D, E, and F are all correct.)

Incorrect answer choice A speaks to the possible misconception that the Sun, in and of itself, is the sole source of seasonal changes regardless of its position with respect to Earth. While there *is* variation in the amount of heat and light energy from the Sun, there is absolutely no correlation between this variation and the seasons!

The most obvious and common misconception is that answer choice B is correct. This misconception is addressed when students make a model (in Session 2.1) that shows Earth's orbit as very nearly circular. Interestingly enough, Earth is closest to the Sun around January 4th and farthest from the Sun around July 4th. Earth is only about 1.5% closer to the Sun when it is winter in the Northern Hemisphere and about 1.5% farther from the Sun when it is summer in the Northern Hemisphere.

A more subtle misconception might be indicated by a student responding that answer choice C is correct. This could indicate that the student is aware that Earth's axis is tilted, and for that reason, the student mistakenly thinks the United States is closer to the Sun in June. Answer C is an incorrect response partly because the distance closer to the Sun represented by the tilt is insignificant as an explanation for why it is hotter (which is what the question is asking). This response still focuses on *distance* as the primary cause of seasons and indicates a lack of awareness about the key issue of relative scale. The student does not realize that the vast distance between the Sun and Earth makes the tilt of the Earth irrelevant with regard to the distance between various places on Earth and the Sun. Even the whole diameter of Earth (about 12,000 kilometers) is an insignificant distance when compared with the distance from Earth to the Sun (about 150,000,000 kilometers), so a distance less

continued on page 279

SESSION 2.1 Introducing Seasons and the Pre-unit 2 Questionnaire

Some students may already know that the average distance from Earth to the Sun is closer to 93 million miles. If this is raised, say that the scale being used here (one yard = two million miles) is approximate, and this difference (between 93 and 100 million) does not affect the scale-model drawing.

a. **Draw a rectangle.** It can be any size.

b. **Divide the rectangle into two equal parts by drawing a vertical line.** Label the line with a "50" to represent the football field's 50-yard line.

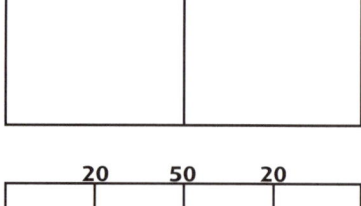

c. **Divide each of those parts in half with two more vertical lines.** Label each of these new yard lines with a "20."

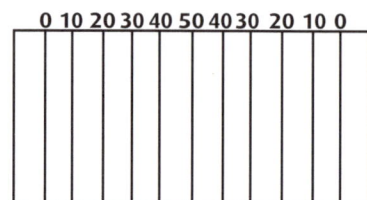

d. **Draw two more vertical lines in each part, dividing each into thirds.** Label these new yard lines "0," "10," "30," and "40." Say that the 0-yard lines represent the goal lines. The area between the goal lines and the ends of the rectangle are the end zones.

7. **One yard equals two million miles.** Say that for this scale model, one yard on the football field equals about two million miles, so *each* 10-yard distance between yard lines on the field represents 20 million miles!

8. **Put the Sun and Earth on the field.** Ask, "Using this scale, if the Sun is roughly a million miles in diameter, how large should it be in this scale model?" [one-half yard.] Have students draw a one-half yard wide Sun (it should be very small) in the middle of their 50-yard lines. Next, say that Earth is roughly 8,000 miles across, which would be less than 1/200 of a yard on this scale. Have students draw a tiny dot on the 0-yard line (or goal line) to represent Earth.

9. **Discuss the distance between Earth and Sun.** Ask how far Earth is located from the Sun in this model. [50 yards.] Remind students that since a yard represents two million miles in this model, the distance between Earth and the Sun is about 100 million miles. (For added visualization, tell the class that this distance is roughly equivalent to driving around the circumference of Earth 4,016 times!)

10. **The Sun-Earth distance stays nearly constant as Earth orbits the Sun.** Show the class the Distances from Earth to Sun transparency and ask, "Does the distance from Earth to Sun change a lot throughout the year?" Point out that the closest distance is about 147,000,000 km, and the farthest is 152,000,000 km. The difference is about 5,000,000 out of 150,000,000, or 1/30 or 3%. Say that the variation in Earth-Sun distance is less than a yard on the scale of their football field model. So, on the opposite goal of the football-

TEACHER CONSIDERATIONS

ABOUT THE PRE-UNIT 2 QUESTIONNAIRE RESPONSES
continued from page 277

than the whole diameter (such as that caused by the tilt) is even less significant. As noted above, the actual Sun-Earth distance varies by about 1.5%—or from 147,000,000 km to 151,000,000 km—and even that difference of about 4 million kilometers is not significant as an explanation for seasons.

That leaves answers D, E, and F, all of which are correct. As the activities in this unit will demonstrate, there are two main factors responsible for Earth's seasons. Both are related to the tilt of Earth's axis, but **neither are related to changes in distance.** The two factors responsible for Earth's seasons are:

- **More daylight hours.** The tilt of Earth means that portions of Earth where there is summer are facing more toward the Sun, making for more hours of daylight. Because the United States is facing more toward the Sun in June and away from the Sun in December, there are more hours of daylight in June.

- **Angle and concentration of light.** At the same time, during summer, the Sun's position in the sky is higher, increasing the angle of incidence of sunlight. As the activity in Session 2.5 will show, this increases the concentration of light on the ground, so the ground gets warmer.

4. In this Sun-Earth drawing, which picture of Earth best shows its size and distance from the Sun? (The correct answer is C.)

C is correct because it most accurately represents the great distance between the Sun and Earth and the great difference in size between the two.

5. These two pictures show the same tree on two different days at noon. Why do the Sun's rays come in at different angles? Explain why this occurs.

Students' explanations should include the idea that because Earth tilts toward or away from the Sun at different times of the year, sunlight strikes the ground at steeper or shallower angles. Earth's axis is tilted toward the Sun around the time of the summer solstice, causing a steeper angle of sunlight (i.e., more intense). Around the winter solstice, Earth's axis is tilted away from the Sun, causing a shallower angle of sunlight (i.e., less intense). As students will learn in this unit, Earth's axis is always tilted toward Polaris, the North Star. As Earth travels around the Sun, one hemisphere or the other is titled more toward the Sun, depending on where Earth is in its orbit. The

continued on page 281

SESSION 2.1 Introducing Seasons and the Pre-unit 2 Questionnaire

field, Earth's orbit would pass near the 1-yard line (instead of the 0-yard line). Have students place another tiny dot on the 1-yard line near the opposite goal and then have them draw a circle connecting the two dots to represent Earth's orbit around the Sun. Emphasize that the circle should be nearly round (nearly a circle), since the distance from Sun to Earth changes very little. That means that parts of the circle (top and bottom) should go well beyond the sidelines of the football field.

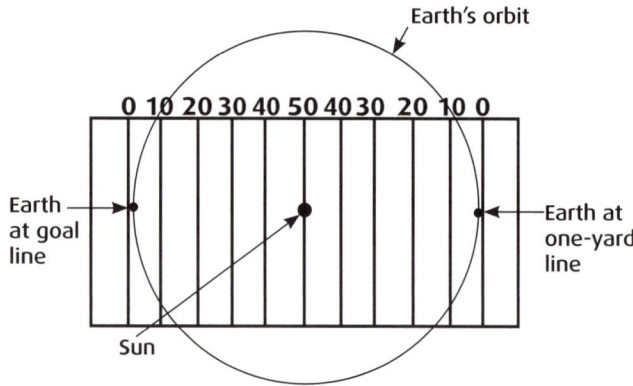

11. **Does Earth's distance from the Sun change enough to cause the seasons?** Ask, "How would you describe Earth's orbit?" [It is very nearly circular.] Ask next, "Is the Sun in the middle of Earth's orbit, or is it located nearer to one side of Earth's orbit?" [It's very nearly in the middle of Earth's orbit.] Post on the concept wall, under Key Space Science Concepts:

Earth travels around the Sun in a nearly circular orbit.

The Sun is very close to the center of Earth's orbit.

12. **Look again at Question #2 on the Pre-unit 2 Questionnaire.** Show the Pre-unit 2 Questionnaire transparency of Question #2. Ask students to think about how they would describe the shape of Earth's orbit now and then have them discuss their answers and reasoning with a partner. (Students will discuss Question #2 again at the beginning of Session 2.2, so omit this step if time is short.)

13. **(Optional) If time permits, do the hula-hoop demonstration for your students from Session 2.2.** If you have a few minutes, show your students the hula-hoop demonstration (page 286 Step #4) from Session 2.2.

14. **Students keep papers in a folder.** Tell students they will each have a folder in which to keep their work for this unit. Hand out the file folders. Have students write their names on their folders and put their football-field models inside them. Collect the folders. After class, add the students' Pre-unit 2 Questionnaires to their folders.

TEACHER CONSIDERATIONS

ABOUT THE PRE-UNIT 2 QUESTIONNAIRE RESPONSES
continued from page 279

Northern Hemisphere is tilted toward the Sun during its summer and is tilted away from the Sun when it is experiencing winter. The opposite is true for the Southern Hemisphere

6. Imagine that there are two Earths. One Earth is where our Earth is. The other Earth is 8,000 miles closer to the Sun. Which place on these two Earths would be hotter—point A or point B? Explain your answer. (The correct answer is A.)

The correct answer is A because the intensity of sunlight is higher there, due to the steeper angle of incidence of the light at that location. While location B is closer to the Sun, the difference in distance (8,000 miles out of 93,000,000 miles) is insignificant as a factor in affecting the intensity of light hitting the ground.

QUESTIONNAIRE CONNECTION

Questionnaire Connections allow you to assess your students' understanding of key unit concepts through the discussion of questions on the Pre-unit 2 Questionnaire. **Do not give out the correct response to your students**. Instead, ask them to consider the question, and whether they would change their answer (and why) based on what they have just learned. Additional information to help you interpret your students' responses to the questions can be found in the About the Pre-unit 2 Questionnaire Responses on page 275.

SESSION 2.2

Does Variation in the Sun-Earth Distance Cause Seasons?

Overview

This session tackles, once again, the common misconception that the varying distance between Earth and the Sun is a cause for seasons. Two activities in this session provide additional evidence for arguing against this reasoning. Students first review what they learned about the shape of Earth's orbit from Session 2.1. The class then analyzes year-long temperature graphs for different locations around the world. They discover that the pattern of temperature change from summer to winter in one hemisphere is reversed in the opposite hemisphere—further evidence that the Sun-Earth distance is not responsible for seasons. Next, the class observes another scale model of the Sun-Earth system and concludes that the Sun-Earth distance is enormous compared with the size of Earth. Later in the unit, this understanding of scale will help students understand that Earth's tilt does not make a significant difference in its distance from the Sun. The session concludes with students in evidence circles discussing the question, "Do changes in the Sun-Earth distance cause the seasons?" Students use what they have learned so far to support their responses. During this session, the key concepts added to the classroom concept wall are:

- *Patterns of average-temperature change (and seasons) are opposite for the Northern and Southern Hemispheres.*
- *Earth's tilt does not significantly change its distance from the Sun.*
- *Scientific explanations are based on evidence gathered from observations and investigations.*

Does Variation in the Sun-Earth Distance Cause Seasons?	Estimated Time
Reviewing the Shape of Earth's Orbit	5 minutes
Temperatures Around the World	15 minutes
A Three-Dimensional Sun-Earth Scale Model	10 minutes
Evidence Circles	15 minutes
Total	**45 minutes**

What You Need

For the class:
- ❑ overhead projector or computer with large-screen monitor or LCD projector
- ❑ prepared key concept sheets from the copymaster packet or CD-ROM file
- ❑ 1 large, round embroidery hoop or hula hoop
- ❑ a world globe
- ❑ transparencies of the Pre-unit 2 Questionnaire (four pages, from Session 2.1)
- ❑ transparency of the Project GLOBE Sample Data from the transparency packet or CD-ROM file

Unit Goals

The seasons are not caused by variations in Earth's distance from the Sun.

Earth's spin axis remains tilted toward Polaris as it orbits the Sun.

Earth's tilt does not significantly change its distance from the Sun.

Seasons are caused by Earth's tilt, which affects the intensity of sunlight and the number of daylight hours at different locations on Earth.

282 • SPACE SCIENCE SEQUENCE 6-8

Session 2.2: Does Variation in the Sun-Earth Distance Cause Seasons?

TEACHER CONSIDERATIONS

PROVIDING MORE EXPERIENCE
If you think your students need more experience thinking about and understanding the shape of Earth's orbit, present the What is the Shape of Earth's Orbit? activity in the optional session, on page 374, in which students learn more about and draw ellipses.

Key Vocabulary

Scientific Inquiry Vocabulary
Evidence
Model
Observation
Prediction
Scale
Scale model
Scientific explanation

Space Science Vocabulary
Equator
Equinox
Hemisphere
Intensity
Latitude
Orbit
Solstice
Spin axis

SESSION 2.2 Does Variation in the Sun-Earth Distance Cause Seasons?

- ❏ transparency of Project GLOBE: Temperatures for Alaska (58°N) from the transparency packet or CD-ROM file
- ❏ transparency of Project GLOBE: Temperatures for Antarctica (63°S) from the transparency packet or CD-ROM file
- ❏ transparency of Project GLOBE: Temperatures for Ecuador (0°) from the transparency packet or CD-ROM file
- ❏ 3 different colored transparency pens
- ❏ a blunt pencil or toothpick (about 1 mm in diameter at the tip) to model Earth
- ❏ 1 ball, 10 cm in diameter (to model the Sun)

For each student:
- ❏ 2 sheets of paper
- ❏ student folder with unit work (from Session 2.1)

Getting Ready

1. **Arrange for the appropriate projector format to display images to the class.** Decide whether you will be using the overheads or the CD-ROM. Set up an overhead projector or a computer with a large-screen monitor or LCD projector. (Note: You will need an overhead projector for the Temperatures Around the World demonstration in which you overlay several transparencies.)

2. **Prepare the key concept sheets.** Make a copy of each key concept and have them ready to post on the classroom concept wall during the session.

3. **Color-code the Project GLOBE temperature graphs.** Use a different colored transparency pen to color the temperature graphs for the three Project GLOBE transparencies: Alaska (58°N), Antarctica (63°S), and Ecuador (0°).

TEACHER CONSIDERATIONS

TEACHING NOTES
The key concepts can be posted in many different ways. If you don't want to use sentence sheets, here are some alternatives:

- Write the key concepts out on sentence strips.
- Write the key concepts out before class on a posted piece of butcher paper. Cover each concept with a strip of butcher paper and reveal each one as it is brought up in the class discussion.

SESSION 2.2 Does Variation in the Sun-Earth Distance Cause Seasons?

4. **Decide on best location.** If you can't pace out 10 meters in your classroom, decide where would be the best place to take the class for the short scale-model activity. Find a spot that will allow you to pace out 10 meters—approximately 10 long strides. If you're lucky, this can be done along a diagonal in the classroom between opposite corners, with some nudging of desk positions. If the classroom is too small, plan to go into the hallway for this demonstration. Another alternative would be to halve the scale of the activity (see page 287).

5. **Prepare scale models of Earth and Sun.** For Earth, use a pencil or toothpick, approximately 1 mm in diameter at the tip. For the Sun, find a ball about 10 cm in diameter.

6. Plan how you will seat students in teams of four for the evidence-circle discussion.

GO! Reviewing the Shape of Earth's Orbit

1. **Review the football-field model from Session 2.1.** Remind the class of the football-field model of the Sun-Earth system. Ask students what they learned about the distance between the Sun and Earth. [Even though the Sun-Earth distance varies by almost 5 million kilometers throughout a year, that's really only a slight variation compared to the overall distance to the Sun of 150,000,000 km.]

2. **Refer to concepts from previous session.** Point to the concept wall and remind students of the key concepts they learned in Session 2.1:

   Earth travels around the Sun in a nearly circular orbit.

   The Sun is very close to the center of Earth's orbit.

3. **Revisit Question #2 on the Pre-unit 2 Questionnaire.** Show the transparency of Question #2 of the questionnaire. If the class did not have time to discuss this question last time, ask students how (and why) they would answer this question now.

4. **Demonstrate how a circle might appear to be a more elongated ellipse.** Use the hula hoop or large embroidery hoop to demonstrate how a circular orbit can appear to be elliptical, depending on the angle at which you view it. Ask the class why someone might choose answer C or D for Question #2 on the questionnaire. [Drawings of the Sun-Earth system often make the planet's orbit look like a skinny ellipse, because the orbit is drawn as viewed at an angle—from the side and a little bit above.]

TEACHER CONSIDERATIONS

TEACHING NOTES

If a 10-meter distance doesn't fit in your classroom, and you don't have the option of taking your class to another location, halve the model's scale:

- Scale size of Earth: 0.5 mm (the tip of a ballpoint pen might work)
- Scale size of Sun: 5 cm (use a 2" polystyrene ball)
- Scale size of Sun-Earth distance: 5 m (or five giant steps)

Some students may quibble with drawings used in Question #2 of the Pre-unit 2 Questionnaire, insisting that the figures for answers A and B are actually perfect circles, and that they know Earth's orbit is not perfectly circular. Answer A is the correct answer, but you don't need to state that just yet, as students can and should share and discuss why they may still prefer any of the other answers. But in facilitating the discussion, here are some considerations for addressing the plausible student idea that answer A (or B) can't be correct because it inaccurately illustrates a perfect circle. If you refer to the football-field model of the Sun-Earth system from Session 2.1, you can point out how much a near-circle can look like a perfect circle. As humans, we can't easily distinguish, visually, the subtle differences between circles and nearly circular ellipses. They all look like circles, unless one takes a ruler out to measure or knows ahead of time that they're looking at an non-circular ellipse. With Question #2, answer A best represents the Sun-Earth system as viewed from above, since it best illustrates the real shape of Earth's orbit (very nearly circular), and because it places the Sun at the center.

SCIENCE NOTES

Misleading illustrations showing Earth around the Sun in a seemingly elliptical orbit can be found in many sources, including children's books, school and college textbooks, and on the web (try an image search using key words such as *Sun, Earth, seasons, orbit*.) These illustrations often have the positive intention of trying to show Earth in different seasonal positions in its orbit and, at the same time, show Earth's axial tilt. By using a viewing perspective from above and to the side, the illustrations take a nearly circular orbit and make it appear elongated and elliptical. Young students (and many adults) tend to be strong visual learners, so the misleading shape of Earth's orbit tends to stick in their minds rather than any caption or description that may explain the figure and its viewing perspective. A widely varying Sun-Earth distance, also as commonly illustrated, has similar impact on learners who then tend to incorporate their intuitions about how the *distance* from a heat source (such as a campfire) has to be the reason for feeling warmer or cooler. In this way, misleading Sun-Earth illustrations lead to and enhance the common misconception that a varying Sun-Earth distance is the reason for seasons.

SESSION 2.2   Does Variation in the Sun-Earth Distance Cause Seasons?

5. **Reveal that Earth is actually closest to the Sun when it's winter in the Northern Hemisphere.** Tell students that not only does the distance from Earth to the Sun not change much relative to the entire distance, but Earth is actually slightly closer to the Sun around January 4th, which is during winter in North America! (This date can range from January 2nd to January 5th.)

Temperatures Around the World

1. **Gather more evidence that the Sun-Earth distance is not what causes seasons.** Say that some people may need extra evidence that the seasons are not caused by Earth's changing distance from the Sun. Tell the class that today they will look at a year's worth of temperature data from cities around the world and use that data as evidence when thinking about the causes of seasons.

2. **Introduce Project GLOBE.** Tell the class that through an international project known as Project GLOBE, students in many different schools around the world have been measuring and recording the temperature at their location throughout the year.

3. **How to read Project GLOBE data.** Show the Project GLOBE Sample Data transparency. Say that this is an example of the kind of data students are collecting. Point out the following information: the city (Chalatenango), country (El Salvador), and school (Escuela Rural Mixta), as well as its latitude (14°N) and longitude (89°W). Tell students that the list of temperatures shown are *average* monthly temperatures. This means that these measurements are not just the average for one day, but the average for a whole month.

4. **Looking at temperature data for a Northern Hemisphere location.** Hold up the world globe and ask a student to point out the Northern and Southern Hemispheres. Have another student point out Alaska on the globe and ask, "In which hemisphere is Alaska located?" [Northern.] Show the Project GLOBE: Temperatures for Alaska (58°N) transparency. Orient students to the temperature and month axes on the graph. Ask, "What patterns do you see in this temperature graph?" Accept all observations. Ask, "Which months have the lowest average temperature?" [December and January.] Ask, "Which months have the highest average temperature?" [July and August.]

Project GLOBE Sample Data

Chalatenango, El Salvador
Esculea Rural Mixta
Latitude: 14°N
Longitude: 89°W
Elevation: 1,700m

Month	Year	Avg. Temp
Oct	1997	16.9
Sept	1997	16.5
Aug	1997	16.3
July	1997	15.7
June	1997	15.7
May	1997	16.0
April	1997	15.3
March	1997	15.5
Feb	1997	15.4
Dec	1996	15.1

TEACHER CONSIDERATIONS

PROVIDING MORE EXPERIENCE

Students can successfully complete the Temperatures Around the World activity with only a basic understanding of latitude and longitude. However, if time permits, you may want to provide a fuller understanding of these terms. Latitude lines are drawn horizontally, parallel to the Equator. *Latitude* indicates how far a location is north or south of the Equator. *Longitude* indicates how far a location is east or west of the Prime Meridian, which is the north-south line that runs through Greenwich, England and West Africa. You may want to point out the difference between the apparent size of Antarctica on the globe and the flat map. The difference is due to map distortion resulting from the translation of a three-dimensional globe surface to the two-dimensional flat map. You may also want to make sure that students understand what the Northern Hemisphere and Southern Hemisphere are.

Strengthening Understanding of a World Coordinate System: Latitude and Longitude

If your students need a better understanding of and proficiency with finding things on Earth by latitude and longitude, spend some extra time having them practice locating places on Earth by specifying latitude and longitude coordinates. There are many ways to do this. Here are two suggestions:

- Have each student choose a particular continent, write down the coordinates (latitude and longitude) of some place within that continent, and then challenge a partner to determine what continent it is, giving only the coordinates and a world map. This could also be done with countries or cities.

- Call out the coordinates of a particular city and have students find what city it is. The first student to find the correct city gets to choose and call out the coordinates of the next city.

SESSION 2.2   **Does Variation in the Sun-Earth Distance Cause Seasons?**

5. **Looking at temperature data for a Southern Hemisphere location.** Hold up the world globe again and have a student point out Antarctica on the globe. Ask, "In which hemisphere is Antarctica located?" [Southern.] Show the Project GLOBE: Temperatures for Antarctica (63°S) transparency. Ask, again, for the months with the lowest average temperature and the highest average temperature.

6. **Compare temperature graphs from both hemispheres.** Now, overlay the Project GLOBE: Temperatures for Alaska (58°N) transparency over the Project GLOBE: Temperatures for Antarctica (63°S) transparency. Give students a chance to analyze what they see. Students should notice that the temperature graph patterns are opposite for the Northern and Southern Hemispheres. Point out that in the Southern Hemisphere, the hottest months are December through February, when it's winter in the Northern Hemisphere. Ask, "Where we live, what season is it in July?" [Summer.] Ask, "In the Southern Hemisphere, what season is it in July?" [Winter.]

7. **Looking at temperature data for an equatorial location.** Ask the class, "What do you think the temperature graph for a place right on the Equator would look like?" [There would not be much variation in temperature through all the seasons.] Overlay the Project GLOBE: Temperatures for Ecuador (0°) transparency on top of the other two transparencies. Confirm with students that there is not much variation in temperature throughout the year at Ecuador's location.

8. **Students summarize findings in writing.** Hand out a sheet of paper and a pencil to each student and have them write the title, "Temperatures Around the World" on their papers. Have students write a summary of what they observed about the graphs and what the graphs reveal about temperature patterns around the world at different times of the year. (These papers will be used in the evidence-circle activity at the end of the class session.) Post on the concept wall, under Key Space Science Concepts:

   Patterns of average-temperature change (and seasons) are opposite for the Northern and Southern Hemispheres.

9. **Address any comments about Earth's tilt as the cause of seasons.** If any students suggest that Earth's tilt causes the Northern Hemisphere to be closer to the Sun in summer, tell them that the next activity will help them decide if this is the case.

TEACHER CONSIDERATIONS

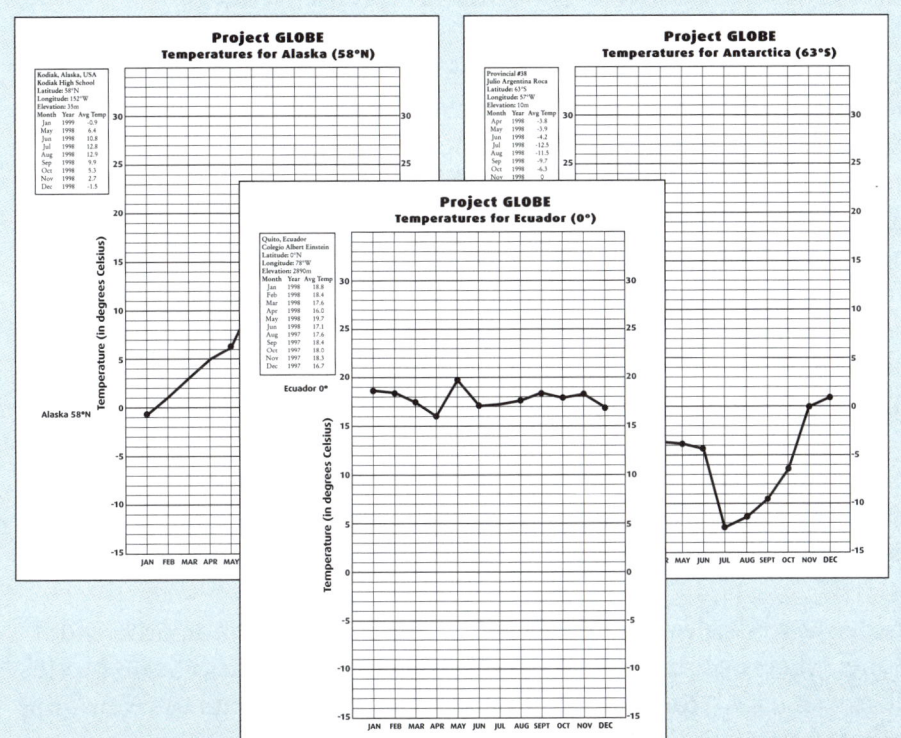

SESSION 2.2 Does Variation in the Sun-Earth Distance Cause Seasons?

A Three-Dimensional Sun-Earth Scale Model

1. **Another scale model, this time in three dimensions.** Tell the class they will now observe another scale model of the Sun and Earth that will help them to further decide if a varying Sun-Earth distance is the reason that seasons occur. (Move the class to another location for this activity, if you've decided to do so.) Tell the class that in this model, 1 cm represents 140,000 km. Have a student hold up the pencil or toothpick and tell the class that the tip of the pencil (or toothpick) represents Earth in this model. (Be sure that students understand that Earth is spherical.) Explain that although Earth in this model is bigger than the tiny dot they drew in their football-field models, it is still small—only about 1 mm in diameter.

2. **Students guess size of model Sun.** Ask, "At this scale, how big do you think the Sun would be?" Accept several guesses. Hold up the 10-cm ball and say that the ball represents the Sun in this model.

3. **Students write down scale sizes for this model.** On the other side of their sheets of paper, have students write "Sun-Earth Scale Model Measurements." Read aloud the following for students to record on their of paper:

   - Scale size of Earth: 1 mm
   - Scale size of Sun: 10 cm
   - Scale of model: 1 cm ≈ 140,000 km

4. **Students guess the distance between Earth and Sun in this model.** Ask, "At this scale, how far away from Earth do you think the Sun should be?" Accept several answers and then reveal that in this model, the Sun would be about 10 meters away from Earth. Have students add to their papers:

   - Scale distance between Earth and the Sun: 10 m

5. **Pace out distance to Sun.** Tell students that a meter is roughly one large step. Have a student hold the model Sun and pace off roughly 10 giant steps away from a student holding the model Earth. Ask the class what this model shows about the distance between the Sun and Earth. [The distance between them is huge, compared to the size of Earth or the Sun.] Make sure students understand that the 1-mm Earth would orbit the Sun, staying about the same distance from the 10-cm Sun. (If you have moved the class to another location, return to the classroom.)

One teacher said, "One student jumped up in the middle of class and yelled, 'I get it! I finally get it!' The rest of the class was startled by her display, but it opened up a great discussion about whether the students actually did get the concepts of the Earth's size and distance to the Sun."

TEACHER CONSIDERATIONS

TEACHING NOTES

This Sun-Earth scale model is nearly identical to the one presented in Unit 1, Session 1.2. If you've already covered Unit 1 with your students, they will only need a brief review of the model. To save time, you can set up this model ahead of time. Pace out 10 m before class, making note of any classroom landmarks at either end of that distance. During class, point out the landmarks so your students can visualize what 10 m looks like.

PROVIDING MORE EXPERIENCE

If time allows, you might want to ask students to compute the scaled diameters and distances of objects in the model. (The Moon is optional.)

	Diameter (km)	Distance from Earth (km)
Earth	12,750	0
Moon	3,480	384,400
Sun	1,390,000	149,600,000

If the Sun will be represented by a 10-cm diameter ball, the scale of the model is:

(1,400,000 km) ÷ (10 cm) = 140,000 km/cm

This scale can also be expressed as: 1 cm = 140,000 km, or 1 cm in this model represents 140,000 km. (Note: Rounding the Sun's diameter up to 1,400,000 km provides an easier number to work with.)

Scaled sizes and distances:

	Diameter (km)	Distance from Earth (km)	Scale Diameter	Scale Distance from Earth
Earth	12,750	0	1 mm	0
Moon	3,480	384,400	0.25 mm	2.75 cm
Sun	1,390,000	149,600,000	10 cm	10.7 m

SESSION 2.2   Does Variation in the Sun-Earth Distance Cause Seasons?

6. **Look again at Question #4 on the Pre-unit 2 Questionnaire.** Show the Pre-unit 2 Questionnaire transparency. Have students discuss which answer choice they think most accurately represents the size and distance of Earth from the Sun.

7. **Does Earth's tilt make a significant difference in Earth's *distance* from the Sun?** Ask students if any of them have heard about Earth's tilt. Tell them that the United States does tilt toward the Sun in the summer, but ask, "Do you think the tilt of Earth really makes the United States closer to the Sun in the summer to make a big difference in temperature?" Students should start to see that the tilt of Earth makes a negligible difference in the vast distance from Earth to the Sun. (If your students are having difficulty understanding this, have one student hold the model Sun and pace out 10 m from a student holding the model Earth, slightly tilted.)

8. **Earth's tilt doesn't make a significant difference in the Sun-Earth *distance*.** Explain that tilt doesn't really change the *distance* from Earth to the Sun. Although one side of Earth is a little closer to the Sun, it's a minuscule difference in distance compared to the whole distance from Earth to the Sun—and this isn't why we experience seasons. **Point out that there is *something else* about Earth's tilt that does have something to do with why we have seasons, and the class will learn more about this later on in the unit.** Post on the concept wall, under Key Space Science Concepts:

   Earth's tilt does not significantly change its distance from the Sun.

Evidence Circles

1. **Introduce evidence circles.** Tell the class that now they will have the opportunity to discuss a question about seasons in small groups called evidence circles. Tell them that during their discussions they should behave like scientists—they should listen carefully to one another, discuss cooperatively, and ask questions. If students are not already seated in groups of four, reseat them for this activity.

2. **Do changes in distance between the Earth and Sun cause the seasons?** Tell students they will discuss the following question in evidence circles: "Do changes in the Sun-Earth distance cause the seasons?" Tell them that each student must provide evidence to back up their answer, whether it is yes or no.

TEACHER CONSIDERATIONS

QUESTIONNAIRE CONNECTION
Questionnaire Connections allow you to assess your students' understanding of key unit concepts through the discussion of questions on the Pre-unit 2 Questionnaire. **Do not give out the correct response to your students**. Instead, ask them to consider the question and whether they would change their answer (and why) based on what they have just learned. Additional information to help you interpret your students' responses to the questions can be found in the Teacher Considerations section in Session 2.1, page 275.

TEACHING NOTES
When the Northern Hemisphere is tilted toward the Sun, it is, technically, closer to the Sun than the Southern Hemisphere. But the tilt brings the Northern Hemisphere closer to the Sun by a distance that is less than the diameter of Earth—12,750 km. This is negligible when compared with the overall distance to the Sun, 149,600,000 km. You might want to have your students calculate the percent difference. You may also want to point out that the change in distance due to the tilt is much smaller than the change due to variations in orbital distance (as seen with the football-field model activity in Session 2.1). The change in distance from the Sun represented by orbital variation is about 1.5%—a change in distance of +/- 2 million km. If that magnitude of difference is not enough to account for the seasons, then a 12,750-km change (from the tilt effect) certainly is not!

Option: Depending on your students' experience with group discussions, you may want to give them some time before the evidence-circle activity to look over their notes individually, consider their ideas, and think about the evidence they might use to support their points of view.

ASSESSMENT OPPORTUNITY
EMBEDDED ASSESSMENT: EVIDENCE-CIRCLE RESPONSES: DO CHANGES IN THE SUN-EARTH DISTANCE CAUSE THE SEASONS?
Students' written responses to the evidence-circle question can be used as an embedded assessment. See the scoring guide on page 104 in the Assessment section.

SESSION 2.2 Does Variation in the Sun-Earth Distance Cause Seasons?

3. **Define *scientific evidence*.** Ask, "What is scientific evidence?" Accept a few responses then explain that *scientific evidence* is something that can be observed, tested, and verified by scientists. Say that a scientific explanation needs to be based on evidence. You need evidence to form an explanation for something. Post on the concept wall, under Key Scientific Inquiry Concepts:

   Scientific explanations are based on evidence gathered from observations and investigations.

4. **Students use evidence gathered from activities.** Tell students that they have gathered enough evidence so far to discuss the question, "Do changes in the Sun-Earth distance cause the seasons?" Tell them they can use the following as evidence for their discussions: their notes about the football-field scale model, their analysis of graphs showing average temperatures around the world, and their list of scale measurements from today's scale model.

5. **Explain procedure for evidence circles.** Explain how an evidence circle works. Students take turns answering the question, providing reasons for their answers. Other students say whether they agree or disagree and provide **evidence** for why they agree or disagree with an answer. Students should be courteous with one another and take turns speaking. Say that it's okay to disagree about their answers, but students must give evidence for their opinions.

6. **Scientists are open to changing their minds based on evidence.** Tell students that the main point of the evidence circles is to think about and discuss ideas and evidence in order to find the best explanation for something. Say that one of the signs of a true scientist is the ability to listen to others and change your mind when you find that what you think doesn't match the evidence, or if you find out that there's more evidence in support of another explanation.

7. **Students write down their reasoning.** Tell students that after their group has had a chance to discuss the evidence, each student will write down what they think and *why*. They should answer the question and list all the evidence they have that supports their answer.

TEACHER CONSIDERATIONS

TEACHING NOTES
More About Evidence Circles

Facilitating Discourse. Evidence circles provide a structure for active student discourse—a chance for students to practice using evidence to support explanations and to employ associated scientific language in their talk and writing. As students offer explanations, the teacher or other students ask questions to prompt the connection of explanations to evidence: Explain why you think that... What is your evidence? How does your evidence support your explanation? How could you be more certain? Does anyone agree or disagree?

Scientific argumentation is a key aspect of students' academic development—not only in science—but also in literacy and other domains. Science educators have increasingly paid attention to "the language of argumentation" as they examine student growth in conceptual understanding. Student mastery of academic subjects is also the mastery of those subjects' specialized patterns of language use. One study notes: "Talking offers an opportunity for conjecture, argument and challenge. In talking, learners will articulate reasons for supporting particular conceptual understandings and attempt to justify their views. Others will challenge, express doubts and present alternatives, so that a clearer conceptual understanding will emerge. In such a manner, knowledge is co-constructed by the group..." (Newton et al, 1999). Evidence circles are one way to enhance the level of evidence-based argumentation in the science classroom. If you're interested in learning more, here are a few references:

Driver, R., Newton, P., & Osborne, J. (2000). Establishing the norms of scientific argumentation in classrooms. *Science Education,* 84(3), 287-312.

Minstrell, J., & Van Zee, E. (Eds.). (2000). Teaching in the Inquiry-based science classroom. Washington, DC: American Association for the Advancement of Science.

Newton, P., Driver, R., & Osborne, J. (1999). The Place of Argumentation in the Pedagogy of School Science. *International Journal of Science Education,* 21(5), 553–576.

Osborne, J. F., Erduran, S., Simon, S., & Monk, M. (2001). Enhancing the Quality of Argument in School Science. School Science Review, 82(301), 63-70.

Taasoobshirazi, G., Hickey, D. (2005). Promoting Argumentative Discourse: A Design-Based Implementation and Refinement of an Astronomy Multimedia Curriculum, Assessment Model, and Learning Environment. *The Astronomy Education Review,* Issue 1, Volume 4:53-70. http://aer.noao.edu/AERArticle.php?issue=7&section=2&article=3

SESSION 2.2 Does Variation in the Sun-Earth Distance Cause Seasons?

8. **Pass out paper and student folders.** Pass out a sheet of paper to each student. Have them write the question, "Do changes in the Sun-Earth distance cause the seasons?" Also pass out the folders with students' work from Session 2.1.

9. **Students conduct evidence circles and write.** Provide at least 10 minutes for students to discuss the evidence-circle question and then write their answers and evidence. If you've decided to use this writing assignment as an embedded assessment, see page 104 for the scoring guide.

10. **Collect writing assignments and folders.** Have students place the papers they've written during this session into their folders and then collect the folders. Tell the class they'll have a chance to discuss these ideas further in the next session.

TEACHER CONSIDERATIONS

UNIT 2 • 299

SESSION 2.3
Hours of Daylight and Seasons

Overview

In previous sessions, students learned that changes in the distance between the Sun and Earth do not account for the seasons. This session and the remaining sessions in this unit focus on revealing the factors that *do* result in the seasons. In this session, students share their findings from last session's evidence circles. Teams then look at and graph the number of daylight hours, by month, for cities at different latitudes. This activity reveals a symmetrical pattern of daylight hours that is opposite for the Northern and Southern Hemispheres. Students discover months when the Sun never sets in Alaska and never rises in Antarctica. They also learn about the terms *equinox* and *solstice*. The graphing and data-analysis activities in this session lay the groundwork for students to effectively build a good model for seasons in Session 2.4. During this session, the key concepts added to the classroom concept wall are:

- *For any given latitude, spring and summer days have more hours of daylight, and fall and winter nights are longer.*
- *In the Northern and Southern Hemispheres, day-length changes (and seasons) are opposite one another during the year.*
- *Day-length changes are more dramatic farther away from the Equator.*

Hours of Daylight and Seasons	Estimated Time
Reviewing Evidence Related to the Sun-Earth Distance and Seasons	15 minutes
Graphing Hours of Daylight Data	20 minutes
Analyzing and Discussing Hours of Daylight Graphs	10 minutes
Total	**45 minutes**

What You Need

For the class:
- ❑ overhead projector or computer with large-screen monitor or LCD projector
- ❑ prepared key concept sheets from the copymaster packet or CD-ROM file
- ❑ transparencies of the Pre-unit 2 Questionnaire (four pages, from Session 2.1)
- ❑ a world globe or transparency of the World Map from the transparency packet or CD-ROM file
- ❑ transparency of the Hours of Daylight Sample Data from the transparency packet or CD-ROM file
- ❑ transparency of the Hours of Daylight Graphing Sheet from the transparency packet or CD-ROM file

Unit Goals

The seasons are not caused by variations in Earth's distance from the Sun.

Earth's spin axis remains tilted toward Polaris as it orbits the Sun.

Earth's tilt does not significantly change its distance from the Sun.

Seasons are caused by Earth's tilt, which affects the intensity of sunlight and the number of daylight hours at different locations on Earth.

TEACHER CONSIDERATIONS

TEACHING NOTES

This session requires students to graph and analyze data. Either review graphing with your students or provide additional time for your students to complete the activity.

We sometimes refer to the number of hours of daylight as *length of day*, even though an average day is 24 hours, or approximately the time it takes Earth to spin once on its axis. This is called a **solar day.** (There is another way to measure the length of a day, called the sidereal day, which is 23 hours and 56 minutes, but the solar day is the appropriate one to use in the context of understanding the seasons.)

Key Vocabulary

Scientific Inquiry Vocabulary

Evidence
Model
Observation
Prediction
Scale
Scale model
Scientific explanation

Space Science Vocabulary

Equator
Equinox
Hemisphere
Intensity
Latitude
Orbit
Solstice
Spin axis

SESSION 2.3 Hours of Daylight and Seasons

❏ transparency of the Hours of Daylight Latitude Data from the transparency packet or CD-ROM file
❏ 1 transparency each of the following Hours of Daylight Latitude Graphs: Alaska, Antarctica, Colorado, New Zealand, and Ecuador from the transparency packet or CD-ROM file
❏ 5 different colored transparency pens

For each team of 4–6 students:
❏ 1 copy of the Hours of Daylight Latitude Data student sheet from the copymaster packet or CD-ROM file
❏ an envelope
❏ (optional) an assortment of colored pens

For each student:
❏ 1 copy of the Hours of Daylight Graphing Sheet student sheet from the copymaster packet or CD-ROM file
❏ student folder with unit work (from Session 2.1)

Getting Ready

1. Arrange for the appropriate projector format to display images to the class. Decide whether you will be using the overheads or the CD-ROM. Set up an overhead projector or a computer with a large-screen monitor or LCD projector. (Note: You will need an overhead projector in order to overlay the five Hours of Daylight Latitude Graphs transparencies for the Analyzing and Discussing Hours of Daylight Graphs activity.)

2. Prepare the key concept sheets. Make a copy of each key concept and have them ready to post onto the classroom concept wall during the session.

3. Decide how you will divide the students into teams of 4–6 for the graphing activity.

4. Make a copy of the Hours of Daylight Latitude Data student sheet for each team. Cut the data sheet along the dashed lines and place the pieces into an envelope so each team has an envelope with the pieces of one student sheet.

5. Make a copy of the Hours of Daylight Graphing Sheet student sheet for each student.

6. Color-code the Hours of Daylight Latitude Graph transparencies. Using five different colored transparency pens, color-code the graph lines on the latitude graphs for Alaska, Antarctica, Colorado, New Zealand, and Ecuador.

TEACHER CONSIDERATIONS

TEACHING NOTES

The key concepts can be posted in many different ways. If you don't want to use sentence sheets, here are some alternatives:

- Write the key concepts out on sentence strips.
- Write the key concepts out before class on a posted piece of butcher paper. Cover each concept with a strip of butcher paper and reveal each one as it is brought up in the class discussion.

For the graphing activity, there are several grouping possibilities.

- If your students struggle with graphing, assign each student in a team to a different latitude. Then, have students who are assigned to the same latitude graph their data together. When it comes time to discuss the graphs, have students return to their original groups as the representative for their assigned graph. (Each student will have a different graph to share with their teammates.)

- Alternatively, for students skilled in graphing, have them graph as many latitudes as they can on their Hours of Daylight Graphing Sheet student sheets. Students could also make keys for their graphs.

SESSION 2.3 Hours of Daylight and Seasons

🢂 Reviewing Evidence Related to the Sun-Earth Distance and Seasons

1. **Students share findings from evidence circles.** Remind students that they discussed the question, "Do changes in the Sun-Earth distance cause the seasons?" in evidence circles during the last session. Ask, "What would you say to someone who thinks that we have summer when Earth is closer to the Sun?" Encourage students to share evidence they discussed in their evidence circles that might convince someone that the Sun-Earth distance is not the reason for seasons. Remind students of the posted key concept from Session 2.2:

   Scientific explanations are based on evidence gathered from observations and investigations.

2. **Review key concepts related to the Sun-Earth distance.** Confirm that evidence shows that seasons are not caused by changes in Earth's distance from the Sun. Remind students of the posted key concepts from Sessions 2.1 and 2.2 and point out what evidence each concept provides to show that the Sun-Earth distance is not responsible for seasons:

   Earth travels around the Sun in a nearly circular orbit.

   Earth's orbit is nearly circular. This is evidence that seasons are not caused by changes in Earth's distance from the Sun.

   Patterns of average-temperature change (and seasons) are opposite for the Northern and Southern Hemispheres.

   When it is winter in the Northern Hemisphere, the Southern Hemisphere experiences summer, and vice versa. This is evidence that seasons are not caused by changes in Earth's distance from the Sun.

3. **Does Earth's tilt make a difference in Earth's distance from the Sun?** Remind the class of the scale model in Session 2.2. Ask, "Does Earth's tilt make a significant difference in Earth's distance from the Sun?" [No.] Remind students of the posted key concept:

   Earth's tilt does not significantly change its distance from the Sun.

4. **Revisit Question #1 on the Pre-unit 2 Questionnaire.** Show the Pre-unit 2 Questionnaire transparency. Ask students what they think of the answer choices for Question #1 in light of what they have observed on the Project GLOBE temperature graphs. Have students discuss how they would answer this question now, and why.

TEACHER CONSIDERATIONS

QUESTIONNAIRE CONNECTION

Questionnaire Connections allow you to assess your students' understanding of key unit concepts through the discussion of questions on the Pre-unit 2 Questionnaire. **Do not give out the correct response to your students**. Instead, ask them to consider the question and whether they would change their answer (and why) based on what they have just learned. Additional information to help you interpret your students' responses to the questions can be found in the About the Pre-unit 2 Questionnaire Responses on page 275.

SESSION 2.3 Hours of Daylight and Seasons

Graphing Hours of Daylight Data

1. **An activity to begin investigating what causes seasons.** Tell the class that up until now, they have been focusing on what *doesn't* cause the seasons—now they will begin investigating what *does* cause the seasons.

2. **Questions about daylight hours and different seasons.** Ask students the following questions:

   - Does the Sun always set at the same time each day? [No.]
   - Is the number of hours of daylight the same each day? [No.]
   - At what times of year does the Sun set the latest (and rise the earliest)? [Summer. Don't reveal the answer if no one knows.]
   - At what time of year are the days shortest? [Winter.]

3. **Elicit student ideas about hours of daylight in different locations.** Ask the class, "On any given day, do you think the number of hours of daylight is the same all over the world?" Accept all answers. Tell students that the activity they are about to do will help them to answer this question.

4. **Point out cities with the same latitude.** Using the world globe or World Map transparency, show students some cities that are all at the same latitude of 38°N.

5. **Show Hours of Daylight Sample Data transparency.** Show the Hours of Daylight Sample Data transparency. Point out that the data gives sunrise and sunset times for different months of the year. Explain that the day length listed is the number of actual hours (and minutes) of daylight on the 21st day of each month. Also point out that this data is for a location at the latitude of 38°N.

6. **Demonstrate how to graph the day-length data.** Show the Hours of Daylight Graphing Sheet transparency. Using the information on the Hours of Daylight Sample Data transparency (for 38°N latitude), demonstrate how to graph the data onto the graphing sheet transparency.

7. **Show the day-length data for different latitudes.** Show the Hours of Daylight Latitude Data transparency. Tell students they will be working in groups to graph day-length data for different latitudes. Pass out a pencil and a copy of the Hours of Daylight Graphing Sheet student sheet to each student.

TEACHER CONSIDERATIONS

TEACHING NOTES

All of the following cities are at about 38°N latitude:

- San Francisco, California
- Charleston, West Virginia
- Wichita, Kansas
- St. Louis, Missouri
- Louisville, Kentucky
- Pueblo, Colorado
- Richmond, Virginia
- Sendai, Japan
- Seoul, South Korea
- Tientsin, China
- Izmir, Turkey
- Athens, Greece
- Palermo, Sicily
- Cordoba, Spain
- Lisbon, Portugal

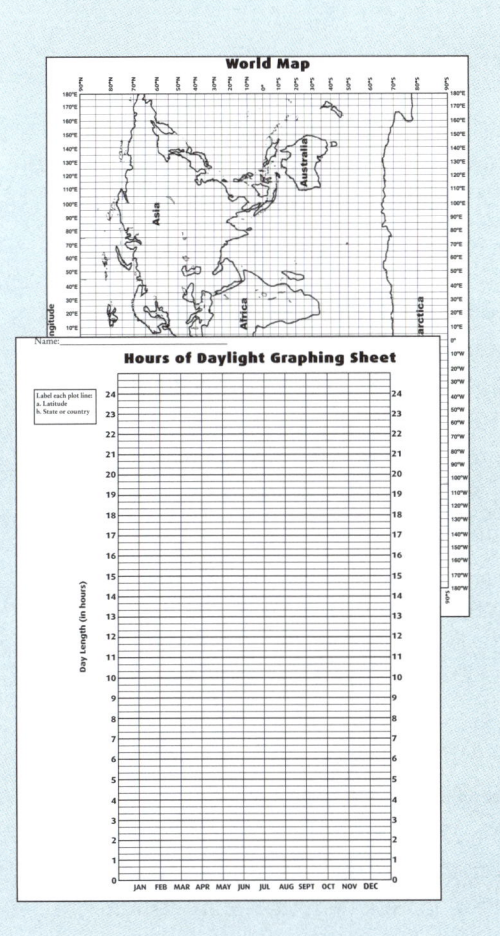

UNIT 2 • 307

SESSION 2.3 Hours of Daylight and Seasons

8. **Divide students into teams of 4–6.** Assign each student in a team to graph a different latitude: either 70°N, 70°S, 38°N, 38°S, or 0°. (For teams of six, have two students graph the same latitude. For teams of four, have students focus on the 70° and 38° latitudes, then the first student done can graph the 0° data.) Point out these five latitudes on the world globe or World Map transparency.

9. **Students who finish early can make more graphs.** Say that students who finish before time is up can graph additional latitude data on their graphing sheet. They should use a different line (such as a dashed or dotted line) or a different colored pen to distinguish between the graphs of different latitudes.

10. **Have teams begin graphing.** Pass out the envelopes containing the cut up Hours of Daylight Latitude Data student sheets to each team. Have teams begin work. Circulate around the classroom and help students as needed.

Analyzing and Discussing Hours of Daylight Graphs

1. **Small groups analyze and compare graphs.** Once everyone has finished at least one latitude graph, ask students to compare their graphs with the others in their group. Tell them to look for patterns. Have students note, in the right-hand margin of their graphing sheet, anything they notice that they think is significant. You may want to prompt students with questions such as:

    - How do hours of daylight compare with hours of night in different places?
    - Are there any months when hours of daylight are equal to hours of night?
    - If there are months when hours of daylight equal hours of night, are they the same months for any location on Earth?

2. **Teams share their analyses and comparisons.** Use the sequence of discussion suggested below or follow your students' lead concerning the order of graphs they would like to compare and discuss. As students share their observations, overlay the transparencies of color-coded Hours of Daylight Latitude Graphs on the overhead projector to show contrasting graphs.

    - **Arctic and Antarctic seasons.** Overlay the Alaska (70°N) and Antarctica (70°S) graph transparencies on the overhead projector. Encourage students to share their observations. Ask, "What do the lines that go up and down steeply tell you?" [At that latitude, day length changes greatly with the seasons.]

TEACHER CONSIDERATIONS

TEACHING NOTES

Have a discussion with your students to discover if any of them have ever visited or lived in a place with very different day lengths than those in your school's region. If time permits, allow some discussion of what it must be like to have no daylight or no darkness for 24 hours.

In order to compare the different Hours of Daylight Latitude Graphs once they are filled out, you will need to use the five transparencies and the overhead projector. Each transparency will overlay the next, so students are able to see the relationship of data among five different locations.

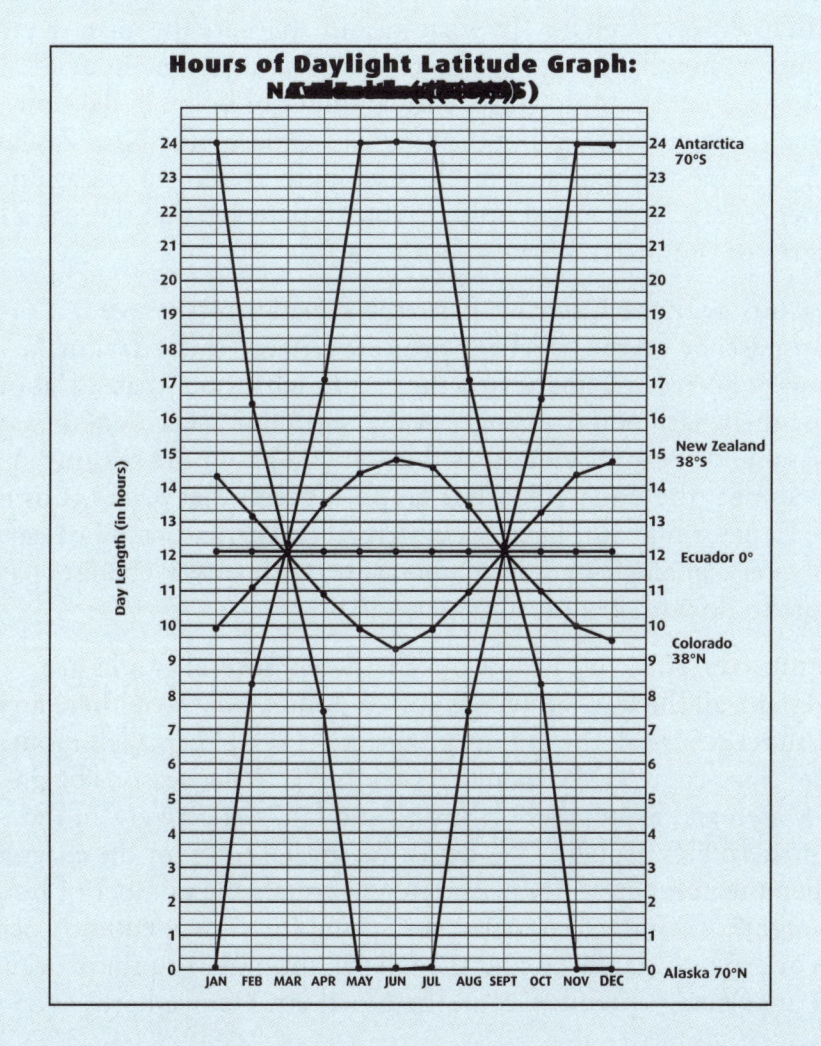

Hours of Daylight Latitude Graph:

Locations shown: Antarctica 70°S, New Zealand 38°S, Ecuador 0°, Colorado 38°N, Alaska 70°N

This is the result of the overlay of the five different transparencies.

One teacher said, "The graph provided a great visual for students. I added the challenge to write on the back their hypothesis of what happened at the points where all the lines on the graph intersected. Most groups made a hypothesis having to do with spring and fall based on the months the intersections happened."

UNIT 2 • 309

SESSION 2.3 Hours of Daylight and Seasons

One teacher said, "Students were very interested to learn that there are places where there could be total darkness or total sunlight for months at a time."

- **Midnight Sun.** If the idea of 24 hours of continuous day or night does not come up, ask, "What does it mean if there are 24 hours of daylight or 24 hours of night (0 hours of daylight)?" Follow up by asking, "Do any of the latitude graphs show certain months where the Sun never comes up (0 hours of daylight)?" [Yes. Alaska and Antarctica.] Tell students that at latitudes where 24 hours of daylight occur, people can see the Sun at midnight. This is sometimes called the *midnight Sun*.

- **Colorado and New Zealand day lengths.** Put the Colorado (38°N) graph transparency on the overhead projector. Ask teams to share their observations. If necessary, prompt the discussion with questions such as: "In what month are there the most daytime hours?" "In what month are there the most nighttime hours?" "In what month or months are the number of hours in daytime equal to the number of hours at night?" Overlay the New Zealand (38°S) graph transparency on the Colorado graph and ask again for observations. Students should be able to perceive that there is a high degree of symmetry between both graphs.

- **Seasons near the Equator.** Place the Ecuador (0°) graph transparency on the overhead projector. Ask, "If the data make a straight horizontal line across the graph, what does that say about how the length of day changes at that latitude?" [Day length stays the same all year.] "What does this tell you about the seasons in places near the Equator?" [The graph suggests that places at or near the Equator may not have seasons at all and actually tend to have only very small changes in temperature, with season changes having more to do with dry or rainy periods.]

- **Equinoxes.** If no one points out that when several graphs are overlaid, all the lines converge at two points, ask, "Are there any latitudes where all the graphs intersect?" [Yes.] "In which months does this occur?" [March and September.] "What seasons begin in March and September?" [Spring and fall, respectively, in the Northern Hemisphere.] "What is the special term for the exact date when the number of hours of daylight equals the number of hours of night?" [Equinox.] Say that the spring (or vernal) equinox occurs on or around March 21, and the fall (or autumnal) equinox occurs on or around September 21 in the Northern Hemisphere.

- **Solstices.** Ask, "Does anyone know the special term for the day of the year when there are the most daylight hours?" [Summer solstice, on or about June 21 in the Northern Hemisphere.] Ask, "What is the special term for the day with the longest night?" [Winter solstice, on or about December 21 in the Northern Hemisphere.]

TEACHER CONSIDERATIONS

TEACHING NOTES

From the data and graphs, one can infer that the Sun never comes up from November 21 through January 21 at latitudes north of 70°N. From May 21 through July 21, the Sun never comes up at latitudes south of 70°S latitude. Likewise, the Sun never sets from May 21 through July 21 at latitudes above 70°N. From November 21 through January 21, the Sun never sets at latitudes south of 70° S.

We often say that summer days are long or winter nights are long, but keep in mind that the summer and winter solstices are technically the beginning of these seasons. The maximum day length falls on the summer solstice, so the spring days leading up to June 21 have similar daylight hours as thee summer days that follow June 21. So, it is most accurate to say that spring and summer days have more hours of daylight. In the same way, fall and winter nights are longer.

SESSION 2.3 Hours of Daylight and Seasons

3. Students summarize, in writing, any *patterns* they've observed. Ask students to turn over their graphing sheets and spend a minute or so summarizing, in writing, the patterns they observed. Students should also make note of the following key concepts as you post them under Key Space Science Concepts:

For any given latitude, spring and summer days have more hours of daylight, and fall and winter nights are longer.

In the Northern and Southern Hemispheres, day-length changes (and seasons) are opposite of one another during the year.

Day-length changes are more dramatic farther away from the Equator.

4. How day length is related to the reasons for seasons. Tell the class that their observations from today will help them better understand the real reasons for seasons in upcoming class sessions. If no students have brought this up in the preceding discussion, remind them that the Sun not only gives us light, but also heat. Say that longer daylight hours mean more time for the Sun to warm that part of the Earth.

5. Collect student work. Collect students' graphs and put them into their folders.

TEACHER CONSIDERATIONS

ASSESSMENT OPPORTUNITY
QUICK CHECK FOR UNDERSTANDING: HOURS OF DAYLIGHT PATTERNS OBSERVED
Students should understand how both latitude and season affect the hours of daylight observed at a particular location on Earth. After students have completed their written summaries, hold a brief class discussion for students to share their findings.

SESSION 2.4
Observing Seasons

Overview

Having explored the Sun-Earth distance, the shape of Earth's orbit, and the differing temperatures and day lengths of various locations around the world, your students have plenty of evidence that Earth's distance to the Sun does not cause seasons. In the unit's remaining sessions, students make models that stand up to all the evidence they've gathered and explain the real reasons for seasons. In this session, the class models seasons with two Earth models: one with no tilt and one with a tilted spin axis. Students then stand in a large circle around a light-bulb Sun with their model Earths and discover how the tilt of Earth's spin axis toward the North Star causes seasons. This model is especially effective in showing what causes seasonal variations in day length. Afterward, students discuss, answer, and write responses to questions about what they've learned. Their written work gives you a tool to assess if they are ready to move on to Session 2.5, in which they will learn about another reason for seasons: the angle and intensity of light reaching Earth. During this session, the key concept added to the classroom concept wall is:

- *Earth's tilted spin axis causes seasonal changes in hours of daylight and night throughout the year.*

Observing Seasons	Estimated Time
A Model with No Tilt	10 minutes
A Tilted Model	15 minutes
Orbiting and Observing Seasons	5 minutes
Discussing the Model and What Causes Seasons	15 minutes
Total	**45 minutes**

What You Need

For the class:
- ❏ overhead projector or computer with large-screen monitor or LCD projector
- ❏ (optional) Space Science Sequence CD-ROM
- ❏ prepared key concept sheet from the copymaster packet or CD-ROM file
- ❏ transparencies of the Pre-unit 2 Questionnaire (four pages, from Session 2.1)
- ❏ a 100-watt incandescent light bulb
- ❏ clip-on socket
- ❏ extension cord
- ❏ 1 copy each of the five mini-posters: Polaris, A, B, C, and D from the copymaster packet or CD-ROM file
- ❏ tape

Unit Goals

The seasons are not caused by variations in Earth's distance from the Sun.

Earth's spin axis remains tilted toward Polaris as it orbits the Sun.

Earth's tilt does not significantly change its distance from the Sun.

Seasons are caused by Earth's tilt, which affects the intensity of sunlight and the number of daylight hours at different locations on Earth.

TEACHER CONSIDERATIONS

TEACHING NOTES

The key concepts can be posted in many different ways. If you don't want to use sentence sheets, here are some alternatives:

- Write the key concepts out on sentence strips.
- Write the key concepts out before class on a posted piece of butcher paper. Cover each concept with a strip of butcher paper and reveal each one as it is brought up in the class discussion.

If your room can be almost completely darkened, consider having students work in teams of 3 or 4 using actual Earth globes for the model. Test this option in advance to see if the dividing line between day and night on the globe (known as the *terminator*) can be easily seen. The terminator is more difficult to distinguish clearly on Earth globes than on white polystyrene balls and typically requires a room with very little ambient or reflected light. If this turns out to be an option for you, it saves in materials and preparation time.

CD-ROM NOTES

Visualizing Seasons. This interactive activity is a simulation of Earth's seasons that can be used by both teachers and students. After the introduction screen explaining the different imaginary dividing lines around Earth, the user is presented with two separate views of a simulated Earth rotating around the Sun and a control screen. The larger window in the simulation is a side view of Earth, with a smaller top view located in the lower right-hand window. Below the side view window, users will find controls that alter the tilt and position of the simulated Earth, and show or hide the equator and tropics. Daylight hours and temperatures for four cities located around the planet are shown in the lower left-hand corner. To locate these cities on the side view of the simulated Earth, click the cities' names to highlight their position and latitude. Data will automatically update once the tilt or month has been changed. The distance between Earth and the Sun is shown in the top view of the simulated Earth and will also update based on the month. To enlarge the interactive to full screen, click CONTROL F in Windows and APPLE F for Macs. Click ESC to exit. Please note: sizes and distance are not to scale in this simulation.

Do not have students use this CD activity until they have finished the modeling activities in this session first.

Key Vocabulary

Scientific Inquiry Vocabulary

Evidence
Model
Observation
Prediction
Scale
Scale model
Scientific explanation

Space Science Vocabulary

Equator
Equinox
Hemisphere
Intensity
Latitude
Orbit
Solstice
Spin axis

SESSION 2.4 Observing Seasons

❑ permanent markers in four different colors: red, green, black, and blue (to mark the polystyrene balls) OR a red permanent marker and small dot stickers in red, green, black, and blue

For each student:
❑ 1 polystyrene ball
❑ 1 pencil
❑ 1 copy of the Tilted-Earth Model Questions student sheet from the copymaster packet or CD-ROM file
❑ student folder with unit work (from Session 2.1)

Getting Ready

Before the Day of the Activity

1. **Find a space than can be darkened.** For this session, you'll need to darken the room. If this is difficult to do in your own classroom, find and reserve a room that can be darkened.

2. **Test run.** You may want to work with another teacher or do a test run of some of the modeling activities in this session. By doing this, you'll know what to expect and be prepared to help students who are having difficulty.

3. **Prepare a model Earth for each student.** Each polystyrene ball will be a model of Earth. A pencil poked into the ball is used as a handle and also marks the South Pole. Mark each polystyrene ball as described below using permanent markers (so the color will not rub off) and/or colored dot stickers.

   a. **Draw in the Equator using the red marker.** Draw a red line around the circumference of each ball to represent the Equator.

   b. **Mark the North Pole.** Draw a large dot in red (or place a red dot sticker) at the North Pole of the ball.

   c. **Mark a location roughly halfway between the Equator and the North Pole.** Use a green marker to draw a large dot (or place a green dot sticker) at this location. It will represent a mid-latitude city in the Northern Hemisphere.

   d. **Mark a second location at a latitude of roughly 70°N (closer to the North Pole than the Equator).** Use a blue marker to draw a large dot (or place a blue dot sticker) at this location. It will represent a far northerly (Arctic) locale such as Tromsø, Norway or Prudhoe Bay, Alaska.

   e. **Mark one more location halfway from the Equator to the South Pole.** Use a black marker to draw a large dot (or place a black dot sticker) at this location. It will represent a mid-latitude Southern Hemisphere city like Melbourne, Australia.

TEACHER CONSIDERATIONS

TEACHING NOTES
One teacher who was assembling her own materials for this lesson used Ping-Pong balls attached with hot glue to golf tees instead of polystyrene balls stuck on pencils. Although the Ping-Pong balls are smaller, they were adequate for good observations, easy to store, and when the tees broke off they could be easily fixed.

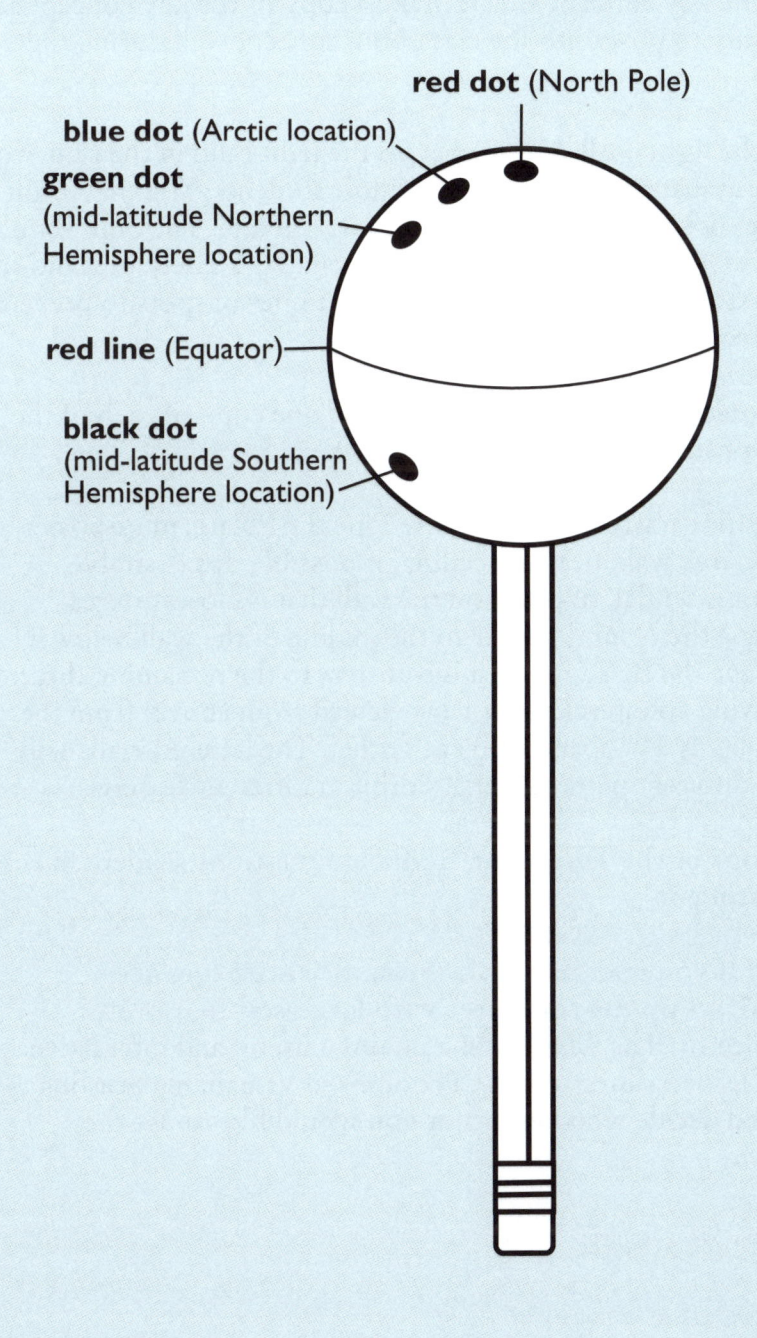

red dot (North Pole)

blue dot (Arctic location)

green dot (mid-latitude Northern Hemisphere location)

red line (Equator)

black dot (mid-latitude Southern Hemisphere location)

SESSION 2.4 Observing Seasons

On the Day of the Activity

1. **Arrange for the appropriate projector format to display images to the class.** Decide whether you will be using the overheads or the CD-ROM. Set up an overhead projector or a computer with a large-screen monitor or LCD projector.

2. **Prepare the key concept sheet.** Make a copy of the key concept and have it ready to post onto the classroom concept wall during the session.

3. **Prepare the light-bulb "Sun."** Set up the light bulb in the center of the room, at just above eye level for most students. You may want to clip the socket to a box on top of a cart or table. The bulb should be clearly visible to all students in the room. As a safety precaution, tape the extension cord to the floor at a number of spots to prevent students from tripping over it.

4. **Make a copies of the mini-posters.** Make one copy of each of the five mini-posters: Polaris, A, B, C, and D.

5. **Tape the mini-posters to the walls.** Tape the Polaris mini-poster high up on one wall, near the ceiling, if possible. It's desirable, though not essential, to put it on the wall that is closest to real North. Tape the A mini-poster to the middle of the wall below Polaris. Tape the B, C, and D mini-posters to the remaining three walls, moving counterclockwise (as viewed from above) from the A wall, roughly 90° apart from each other. The lettered walls will represent different parts of Earth's orbit in different seasons.

6. **Make a copy of the Tilted-Earth Model Questions student sheet for each student.**

7. **Optional: If you plan to use the Space Science Sequence CD-ROM, set up the computer with large-screen monitor or LCD projector.** The CD-ROM contains a useful and interactive visual for this session's activity. Preview the Visualizing Seasons activity and decide whether or not you would like to use the CD-ROM.

TEACHER CONSIDERATIONS

SCIENCE NOTES
Seasons, Solstices, and Equinoxes. The ideas of *solstice* and *equinox* were introduced in Session 2.3 when students examined graphs of the hours of daylight at different times of the year. These are special names for the exact days when Earth reaches certain orbit positions. You may choose to reinforce these ideas by using the words *solstice* and *equinox* while doing the tilted-Earth model activity with your class. The exact day when Earth's axis is tilted directly toward or directly away from the Sun (orbit positions A and C in the model) is called the *solstice*. When the axis is pointed directly away from the Sun (position A), it is the winter solstice in the Northern Hemisphere; when the axis is pointed directly toward the Sun (position C), it is the summer solstice. The name for the special days when the position of Earth in its orbit is exactly halfway between the solstices is *equinox*. Position B represents the spring (or vernal) equinox in the Northern Hemisphere, and position D represents the fall (or autumnal) equinox. In our calendar, the season begins on either an equinox or a solstice. The longest day of summer, with the most intense sunlight on the ground, therefore, is the first day of summer, not the middle of the summer season. Because of the effects of heating over time, the hottest days are usually in the middle of summer, after the summer solstice. Similarly, the coldest part of the year is usually in the middle of the winter season, after the winter solstice.

TEACHING NOTES
Management suggestion. If there is limited classroom space and the class consists of many students, consider having students do this activity in shifts where half the class is in the circle and the other half is seated. This might prevent unnecessary orbital collisions in the dark or one student's body blocking the light of another student's Earth. Before larger groups do this activity, it might be useful to demonstrate to the class (using just one student) how they will move.

SESSION 2.4 Observing Seasons

GO! A Model with No Tilt

1. **More models today to study seasons.** Remind students that in the last session, they looked at hours of daylight data for different latitudes on Earth. In today's session, they will observe two different models to help them understand why the number of hours of daylight changes with different seasons and on different places on Earth. Remind students of the posted key concept from Session 2.1:

   Scientists use models to demonstrate ideas, explain observations, and make predictions.

2. **Introduce parts of the model.** Hold up the light bulb and say that it will represent the Sun in today's models. Hold up a polystyrene ball and say that it will represent the Earth, and that each student will receive a model Earth to observe. Show students how the polystyrene ball can be set on a pencil at its South Pole so that it can be spun around. Say that this represents how Earth rotates on a *spin axis* that runs from the North Pole to the South Pole.

3. **Students should handle the model Earths carefully.** Tell the class that they will need to be quiet and respectful during the modeling activities, so everyone can hear and understand your directions. They should not write on or damage their model Earths and no horseplay with the balls will be tolerated.

4. **Hand out model Earths.** Have students insert pencils into the South Pole end of the polystyrene balls before beginning the activity.

5. **Colored dots on the model Earth represent different locations.** Have students find the following on their model Earths: the Equator, North Pole, South Pole, Northern Hemisphere, and Southern Hemisphere. Explain what the colored dots on their models represent:

   • **The green dot represents a mid-latitude location in the Northern Hemisphere.** Example: Most places in the continental United States. If applicable, tell students that the green dot represents the location of their school.

   • **The black dot represents a mid-latitude location in the Southern Hemisphere.** Example: Australia, South America, or Africa.

   • **The blue dot represents a high-latitude location in the Northern Hemisphere.** Example: Northern Alaska or any other Arctic location.

6. **Have students stand in a large circle around the light bulb with their models.** Remind students to pay attention to your directions. Switch on the light bulb, then turn off the classroom lights.

TEACHER CONSIDERATIONS

TEACHING NOTES

Definition of *axis*. An *axis* is an imaginary straight line around which an object, such as a planet, spins or rotates. Earth's axis is an imaginary line that goes through the North and South Poles.

SESSION 2.4 Observing Seasons

7. **Observing sunrise, sunset, noon, and midnight.** Tell students to slowly spin their model Earths counterclockwise with the spin axis pointed straight up, or vertical. Have them watch their three dot cities move from daylight into night and back again.

   a. **Have students spin their Earths slowly until it is noon at the green dot and then stop.** Ask, "Which way is the green dot facing when it is noon there?" [Toward the Sun.] Circulate around the room, checking models, and ask students to check the positions of each other's models as well.

   b. **Have students spin their Earths slowly until it is sunset at the green dot.** Ask, "How can you tell that it's sunset at the green dot?" [It is rotating from the light into the dark.]

   c. **Have students spin their Earths slowly until it is midnight at the green dot.** Ask, "Which way is the green dot facing when it is midnight there?" [Directly away from the Sun.]

   d. **Have students spin their Earths slowly until it is sunrise at the green dot.** Ask, "How can you tell that it's sunrise at the green dot?" [It is rotating from the dark into the light.]

8. **Observe hours of daylight for the no-tilt model.** As the class slowly spins their models, tell them to observe the three colored dots. Ask, "When Earth's spin axis is vertical, do the green, black, and blue dots stay in the light for the same amount of time or for different amounts of time?" [The same amount of time, roughly.]

9. **Analyze the model and consider tilt.** Ask, "Does this model explain why seasons occur?" [No.] "Why?" [It shows that Earth's spin causes day and night, but it doesn't show why the number of hours of daylight differs at various places on Earth, as shown in last session's graphing activity.] If no one suggests that Earth's axis is tilted (and not vertical), bring this up yourself.

TEACHER CONSIDERATIONS

TEACHING NOTES

Students should spin their Earths in a counterclockwise direction, when seen from above. Later on, students will also circle around, or orbit, the Sun in a counterclockwise direction. This is an accurate reflection of the astronomical fact that the spin of the Earth on its axis goes in the same direction as its revolution around the Sun.

The real tilt angle is always 23.5°. Have students show you their best approximation of a 23.5° tilt. Tell them to try to keep their Earths approximately at that angle, but it's not necessary to be exact.

SESSION 2.4 Observing Seasons

One teacher said, "So students could model the 23.5 degrees, I used a protractor and drew it on the board to let them see the angle of Earth's tilt. When they first circled the model Sun, it was difficult for some to determine the light side or the dark side of the Earth. So, for a few minutes I moved all students to one side of the room and shined the light toward them. They could more easily see how the Sun makes one side of the Earth light up. Then we once again circled the room and moved from Point A to B to C to D."

A Tilted Model

1. **Taking into account Earth's tilt.** Tell students that, in reality, Earth's spin axis is not vertical—it is tilted. Remind them that Earth's spin axis runs from the North Pole to the South Pole.

2. **Earth's spin axis always points toward Polaris.** Reveal that as the Earth spins, its North Pole always points toward Polaris, also called the North Star. So, in fact, Earth's spin axis is not vertical—it is tilted. Point out the Polaris mini-poster taped on the wall. Explain that Polaris is very, very far away, so they should just imagine where Polaris really is and point the axes toward the Polaris wall, not exactly toward the Polaris sign itself. Ask, "Do you know how much the Earth tilts?" [It tilts 23.5 degrees.] Tell the class that there's no need to worry about the exact amount of tilt in this model. It's better to exaggerate the tilt and make it more than 23.5 degrees for now.

3. **Students tilt their models toward Polaris.** Have students align the spin axes of their models toward the direction of the wall with the Polaris mini-poster. Circulate and help students correctly align their spin axes with Polaris.

4. **The A, B, C, and D mini-posters represent different parts of Earth's orbit.** Tell students that in this model, the circle in which they are standing represents Earth's orbit. Point out the A, B, C, and D mini-posters taped to the classroom walls and have students note which letter they are standing closest to. Tell students that their models represent Earth in different parts of its orbit and at different times of the year.

5. **Students share observations from different parts of Earth's orbit.** Have students slowly spin their models and observe the different colored dots as they spin into night and day. Ask a few students from different parts of Earth's orbit to describe what they are observing. Students will have very different answers, depending on where they are standing in Earth's orbit. For example, a student near A might say that the blue dot is in the dark most of the time, while a student near C might observe that the blue dot is in the light most of the time. Accept a few contrasting observations.

6. **Different cities have different day lengths.** Ask, "What do you notice about the day lengths for each colored dot?" [They differ depending on where Earth is in its orbit.] Guide students to discover that, now that Earth is tilted, the dot cities have different day lengths, depending on where they are in Earth's orbit.

324 • SPACE SCIENCE SEQUENCE 6–8   Session 2.4: Observing Seasons

TEACHER CONSIDERATIONS

TEACHING NOTES

The Earth's north spin axis points almost exactly toward the North Star (within a degree). That is why the North Star always stays at the same spot in the sky while all other stars seem to revolve around it.

Confirm that axes are pointed toward Polaris:
Circulate and check that students standing between the Sun and the North Star are keeping their North Poles tilted **away** from the Sun and toward the North Star. Students standing on the opposite side of the "orbit" should have their North Poles tilted **toward** the Sun (and the North Star). Students midway between these positions should have their North Poles pointing sideways from the Sun.

At position A, the Northern Hemisphere is pointing away from the Sun, so it's winter solstice in the Northern Hemisphere and summer solstice in the Southern Hemisphere.

At position B, the Earth's spin axis is pointing neither toward nor away from the Sun. It's spring equinox in the Northern Hemisphere and fall equinox in the Southern Hemisphere.

At position C, the Northern Hemisphere is pointing toward the Sun, so it's summer solstice in the Northern Hemisphere and winter solstice in the Southern Hemisphere.

At position D, the Earth's spin axis is pointing neither toward nor away from the Sun. It's fall equinox in the Northern Hemisphere and spring equinox in the Southern Hemisphere.

	Northern Hemisphere	Southern Hemisphere
Position A	winter solstice	summer solstice
Position B	spring equinox	fall equinox
Position C	summer solstice	winter solstice
Position D	fall equinox	spring equinox

SESSION 2.4 Observing Seasons

7. **Students look more closely at a mid-latitude location in the Northern Hemisphere (the green dot).** Remind students that the green dot represents a mid-latitude, Northern Hemisphere location (and, if applicable, the school's location). Have students slowly spin their tilted models while observing the green dot only. Ask the following questions:

   a. **"Raise your hand if you are observing longer daylight hours for the green dot."** Students near C should raise their hands. Ask, "What season would you say it is for the green dot in that part of Earth's orbit?" [Summer, because the days are longer.]

   b. **"Raise your hand if you are observing longer nights for the green dot."** Students near A should raise their hands. Ask, "What season would you say it is for the green dot in that part of Earth's orbit?" [Winter.]

   c. **"Raise your hand if you are observing equal hours of daylight and night for the green dot."** Students near B and D should raise their hands. Ask students at B and D what season they think it is for the green dot at those locations. Give them the following clue: Earth travels around its orbit from A to B to C to D. Ask, "What season is it for the green dot at B?" [Spring, because Earth is moving in its orbit from A (winter) to C (summer).] Ask, "What season is it for the green dot at D?" [Fall, because Earth is moving in its orbit from C (summer) to A (winter).]

8. **Summarize seasons for the green-dot location.** Check with students at all four orbit positions, asking at each position: "Is the North Pole pointing toward the Sun or away from it?" and "What season is it for the green dot at your location in Earth's orbit?"

9. **Students look more closely at a mid-latitude location in the Southern Hemisphere (the black dot).** Remind students that the black dot represents a mid-latitude, Southern Hemisphere location. Ask them to watch the black dot carefully as they slowly spin their tilted models. Ask, "Is the North Pole pointing toward the Sun or away from it?" and "What season is it for the black dot at your location in Earth's orbit?" Students should realize that the seasons for the black dot (a Southern Hemisphere location) are opposite from the seasons for the green dot (a Northern Hemisphere location).

10. **Compare seasons between hemispheres.** Ask, "Is it ever the same season in both the Northern and Southern Hemispheres?" [No. When it's summer in the Northern Hemisphere, it's winter in the Southern Hemisphere, and vice versa. When it's spring in the Northern Hemisphere, it's fall in the Southern Hemisphere, and vice versa.]

TEACHER CONSIDERATIONS

SESSION 2.4 Observing Seasons

11. **Students look more closely at a high-latitude location in the Northern Hemisphere (the blue dot).** Remind students that the blue dot represents a high-latitude, Northern Hemisphere location, such as northern Alaska. Have them observe the blue dot as they spin their models, then have students in different parts of Earth's orbit report what they see. Explain that near A, the northern Arctic has night for 24 hours. Near C, the northern Arctic receives light for 24 hours; it has midnight Sun. Near B and D, the northern Arctic has day and night. Ask, "What do you think happens near the South Pole?" [Same as the northern Arctic but reversed: almost 24 hours of darkness in Antarctica for students near C and midnight Sun in Antarctica for students near A.]

12. **Verify that number of daylight hours is a reason for seasons.** Confirm with students that Earth's tilt toward Polaris does indeed cause changes in day length, and that this is one of the causes of seasons. Emphasize again that the tilt does not cause seasons because it brings part of Earth closer to the Sun. Instead, the tilt causes seasons because more hours of daylight mean more time for the Sun to shine on and warm up that part of Earth.

Orbiting and Observing Seasons

1. **Students observe day lengths in each season.** Tell the class that now they will observe each season as they model the movement of Earth in its orbit around the Sun. Have students move counterclockwise in their orbit until they are near the next letter: students at A should move to B, students at B should move to C, and so on. Make sure everyone's North Pole is still pointing in the direction of Polaris. Once they're in their new location, have students spin their models and observe:

   • Which hemisphere is pointing toward the Sun?
   • Which hemisphere has longer days? Shorter nights?
   • Which hemisphere has longer nights? Shorter days?
   • Is there midnight Sun or 24 hours of darkness in either the Arctic or Antarctic regions?

2. **Have students move counterclockwise two more times so everyone has a chance to observe all four seasons.** Circulate and check that students have their models correctly aligned with Polaris and continue asking questions as before (Step #1). If time permits, allow for a 1/8 turn shift so students who are generally halfway between the season wall positions get to be more centered between the seasons.

TEACHER CONSIDERATIONS

SESSION 2.4 Observing Seasons

3. **Put away models.** After all students have had a chance to observe each season, turn on the room lights, turn off the light-bulb "Sun," collect the model Earths, and have students return to their seats.

Discussing the Model and What Causes Seasons

1. **Students discuss Tilted-Earth Model Questions.** Pass out the Tilted-Earth Model Questions student sheets and have students work in pairs to discuss the Tilted-Earth Model Questions. Say that although they are discussing the questions with a partner, each student should write out his or her own answers on their student sheets. Allow students about 10 minutes to discuss and write. If you've decided to use this student sheet as an embedded assessment, see page 106 for the scoring guide.

2. **Class discussion of questions.** After students have had a chance to write their responses to the answers, hold a short class discussion. Call on students and ask them to explain their answers to the questions.

3. **Confirm that Earth's tilt contributes to seasons.** Ask the class, "Do you think a planet without a tilted axis would have seasons?" [No, unless the planet's orbit is significantly more elliptical than that of Earth's orbit.] Emphasize once again that Earth's tilt causes the seasons because it results in more hours of daylight—not because it brings parts of Earth closer to the Sun. Post on the concept wall, under Key Space Science Concepts:

Earth's tilted spin axis causes seasonal changes in hours of daylight and night throughout the year.

4. **The angle of sunlight is also a reason for seasons.** If it comes up, tell the class that the angle of sunlight hitting Earth is also a reason for seasons, but ***don't reveal this yet unless a student mentions it***. If it does come up, acknowledge it and tell students that in the next session, the class will explore this further.

330 • SPACE SCIENCE SEQUENCE 6–8   Session 2.4: Observing Seasons

TEACHER CONSIDERATIONS

ASSESSMENT OPPORTUNITIES
CRITICAL JUNCTURE: UNDERSTANDING THE TILTED-EARTH MODEL

By the end of this session, students should realize that Earth's tilt is one of the reasons for seasons, and that it is the tilt that makes days longer or shorter at different times of the year. One way to gauge your students' understanding of this concept is to use the Tilted-Earth Model Questions student sheet as an embedded assessment.

EMBEDDED ASSESSMENT: TILTED-EARTH MODEL QUESTION RESPONSES

The Tilted-Earth Model Questions student sheet can be used as an embedded assessment. See the scoring guide on page 106 in the Assessment section. If student responses indicate that they need additional reinforcement of the concepts presented, go through the Providing More Experience activity outlined below before moving on.

PROVIDING MORE EXPERIENCE

1. **Earth's tilt doesn't make a significant difference in distance to the Sun.** You may notice that some students still think the tilt of Earth causes seasons because it makes one part of Earth much closer to the Sun. Take some time to point out the inaccuracies of scale in the tilted-Earth model they have just observed. Ask, "Is the scale of this model correct?" [No, the real Sun-Earth distance is much greater.]

2. **Have students recall the Sun-Earth scale model from Session 2.2.** Remind them that in that model, Earth was about 1 mm in diameter, with the Sun represented by a 10-cm ball about 10 meters away. Say that it didn't make much difference in the Sun-Earth distance if the tiny Earth was tilted. Ask, "When the North Pole is tilted toward the Sun, is the Northern Hemisphere much closer to the Sun than the Southern Hemisphere?" [No. A few thousand kilometers is not significant compared with the nearly 150 million kilometer distance from Earth to the Sun.]

3. **Repeat today's modeling activity.** If students' responses during this discussion reveal that they do not understand how tilt affects day length, consider taking small groups of students to repeat today's modeling activity while others work on another assignment.

SESSION 2.4 Observing Seasons

5. Discuss Question #3 on the Pre-unit 2 Questionnaire. Show the Pre-unit 2 Questionnaire transparency of Question #3. Ask students which answer choices are supported by the models they have just observed. [D and F.]

6. Collect student work. Collect each student's Tilted-Earth Model Questions student sheet and place these into their folders.

7. Leave A, B, C, D, and Polaris mini-posters taped to the walls for Session 2.5.

TEACHER CONSIDERATIONS

QUESTIONNAIRE CONNECTION
Questionnaire Connections allow you to assess your students' understanding of key unit concepts through the discussion of questions on the Pre-unit 2 Questionnaire. **Do not give out the correct response to your students**. Instead, ask them to consider the question and whether they would change their answer (and why) based on what they have just learned. Additional information to help you interpret your students' responses to the questions can be found in the About the Pre-unit 2 Questionnaire Responses on page 275.

SESSION 2.5
Intensity of Sunlight

Overview
In Session 2.4, students explored how the tilt of Earth causes seasonal changes in the hours of daylight. In this session, they extend the model from the previous session to explore how Earth's tilt causes sunlight to hit the ground at different angles in different seasons and how this changes the intensity of the sunlight on the surface of Earth. At the start of winter (the winter solstice), rays of sunlight strike the ground at a shallow angle and are *less* intense on the ground than the steeper, more perpendicular, rays of sunlight when summer begins (at the summer solstice). Students work in teams to measure and record the intensity of "sunlight" (from a light-bulb "Sun" in the center of the room) at different locations on Earth globes during different seasons. Intensity is measured by counting squares of illumination on a white grid attached to each Earth globe. Students use this data in a closing discussion about how light intensity relates to seasons. This evidence of differences in sunlight intensity, as well as other evidence from previous sessions, will be discussed again in Session 2.6 to give students a more complete picture of the real reasons for seasons. During this session, the key concepts added to the classroom concept wall are:

- *At the beginning of summer, sunlight falls at a steep angle and shines most intensely on Earth's surface.*
- *At the beginning of winter, sunlight falls at a shallow angle and shines least intensely on Earth's surface.*

Intensity of Sunlight	Estimated Time
Investigating Light Intensity	10 minutes
Preparing to Observe and Record Data	10 minutes
Making Observations	10 minutes
Discussing the Data	15 minutes
Total	**45 minutes**

Unit Goals

The seasons are not caused by variations in Earth's distance from the Sun.

Earth's spin axis remains tilted toward Polaris as it orbits the Sun.

Earth's tilt does not significantly change its distance from the Sun.

Seasons are caused by Earth's tilt, which affects the intensity of sunlight and the number of daylight hours at different locations on Earth.

What You Need
For the class:
- ❑ overhead projector or computer with large-screen monitor or LCD projector
- ❑ prepared key concept sheets from the copymaster packet or CD-ROM file
- ❑ 1 copy of the Large Grid mini-poster from the copymaster packet or CD-ROM file
- ❑ a flashlight (one that can project a relatively uniform disk of light)
- ❑ tape
- ❑ the five mini-posters: Polaris, A, B, C, D (from Session 2.4)
- ❑ 4 inflatable Earth globes (at least 20 cm in diameter) with stands

TEACHER CONSIDERATIONS

TEACHING NOTES

Light Intensity. In this session we have referred to intensity of sunlight mainly in terms of intensity on the ground. The actual intensity of sunlight in space, or when measured on a surface perpendicular to the light rays, does not change from season to season. It's only the intensity of rays as they spread out on the ground that changes with the seasons or, for that matter, daily, from morning to afternoon. The intensity of light on the ground is what's important in terms of heating up a particular area of Earth.

Not Direct and Indirect Rays. Light hitting the ground at steep or shallow angles has been traditionally referred to as *direct rays* and *indirect rays*. These terms have led many students to the mistaken idea that there are two kinds of light, or that indirect rays leave the Sun and go somewhere else before they come to Earth. In this session we do not use the terms *direct* and *indirect*, but be aware that your students may have heard them before. Help them make correct sense of the terms. Without a tilt to Earth's axis, there would be no difference in the angle of light hitting the ground at the same latitude in the Northern and Southern Hemispheres on the same day. There would be differences in light intensity as you move from the equator to the poles. Near the equator, the light intensity is greater, and it would be warmer. Near the poles, the light intensity is low, and it would be colder. But at the same latitude north and south, the light intensity, and thus the average temperature, would be the same. This is the same at any orbit position. Without a tilt, sunlight (at all times of year) would hit a city at the same angle, and the light intensity would be the same all year long. Even day length would be the same at all times of year. Without a tilt to Earth's axis, there would be no seasons.

Key Vocabulary

Scientific Inquiry Vocabulary

Evidence
Model
Observation
Prediction
Scale
Scale model
Scientific explanation

Space Science Vocabulary

Equator
Equinox
Hemisphere
Intensity
Latitude
Orbit
Solstice
Spin axis

SESSION 2.5 Intensity of Sunlight

This session requires significant preparation time. We highly recommend that you prepare for this activity well in advance. The good news is that much of the preparation is a one-time job. After it's done, the prep is good for all future classes.

- a drinking straw or coffee stirrer
- 1 copy of the Grid Strip student sheet from the copymaster packet or CD-ROM file
- a permanent red pen
- 4 prepared sunlight mask strips (see Getting Ready)
- 8 drinking straws (not bendable)
- 4 large binder clips (1¾" width)
- a 100-watt incandescent light bulb
- clip-on socket
- extension cord
- transparencies of the Pre-unit 2 Questionnaire (four pages, from Session 2.1)

For each student:
- 1 copy of the Observing Light Intensity student sheet from the copymaster packet or CD-ROM file
- a pencil or pen
- student folder with unit work (from Session 2.1)

Getting Ready

Before the Day of the Activity

1. **Consider arranging to have an adult volunteer help out with this session.** You might find it helpful to have a teacher's aide or parent help you out with the activity.

2. **Practice changing the intensity of light on the grid using the flashlight.** Make a copy of the Large Grid mini-poster. Read through Steps #5 and #6 of Investigating Light Intensity on page 344 and practice changing the intensity of light using the two methods described. If you experience any difficulties, see page 337 for some tips on setting up this flashlight demonstration.

3. **Prepare four Earth globes.** Follow the steps below:

   a. **Inflate the globes.** It is easier to inflate and deflate the globes if you pinch the valve. Squeeze the valve between your teeth while inflating the globe and seal the valve with the plug when it is full. Leave the valve sticking out of the globe—do not press it in flush with the surface of the globe.

   b. **Put each globe on its stand, so that they are tilted at an angle of 23.5 degrees.** Globes may fall out of their stands if loose. To prevent this, cut a ½" long piece of drinking straw or coffee stirrer to help stabilize the globe. If using a drinking straw, put the straw piece over the South Pole bearing. If using a coffee stirrer, insert the piece into the South Pole bearing. Remount the globes onto the stands with the straws or coffee stirrers in place.

TEACHER CONSIDERATIONS

TEACHING NOTES

The key concepts can be posted in many different ways. If you don't want to use sentence sheets, here are some alternatives:

- Write the key concepts out on sentence strips.
- Write the key concepts out before class on a posted piece of butcher paper. Cover each concept with a strip of butcher paper and reveal each one as it is brought up in the class discussion.

You may find that your flashlight does not create a well-defined disk of light. If this is the case, tape a cardboard tube or rolled-up paper tube (about 11" long) onto the end of the flashlight. Use a straw to help keep the flashlight at the same distance from the large grid at different angles. When you practice the demonstration, measure how far away the end of the flashlight or tube needs to be from the large grid in order for it to fill just one 6-cm square. Tape a straw to the end of the tube so that it sticks out just this distance past the end of the tube. Now, when you change the angle of the light, you can keep the light source the same distance away from the paper by keeping the end of the straw touching the wall. (See the photos on page 345.)

Although this activity is written for use with four globes, you can also use eight globes. (If you do, you will need to double most of the materials needed for the session.) More globes means that students will have better access to a globe, but it also means that you will need to set up and check the alignment of four more stations. If you do decide to set up eight globe stations, you should position two stations per wall, with the stations placed somewhat close to one another, so the data collected at each wall will be consistent.

SESSION 2.5 Intensity of Sunlight

Grid Strip

Sunlight Mask Template

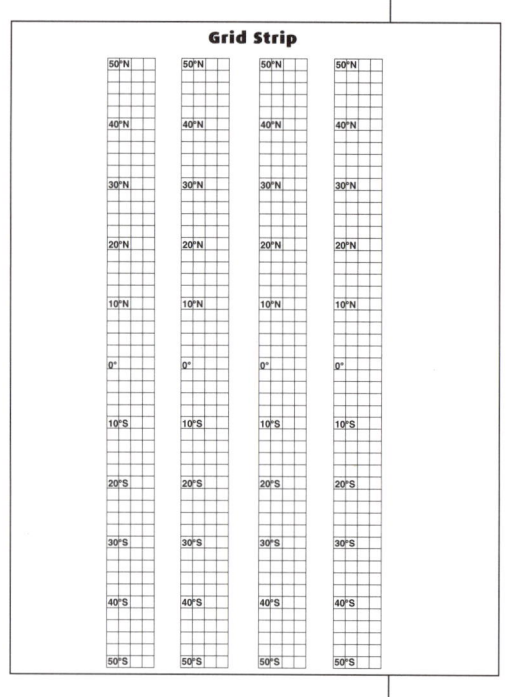

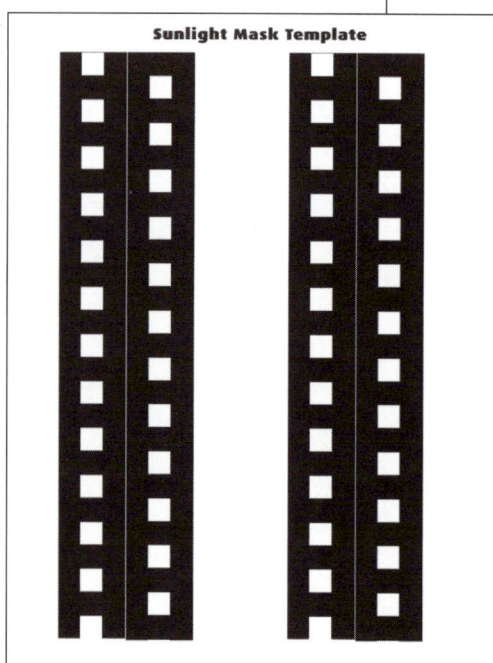

c. **Determine the latitude and longitude of your school.** A map or atlas might have this information. There are also Internet sites that provide longitude and latitude information. (For towns and cities in the U.S., try: http://www.census.gov/cgi-bin/gazetteer)

d. **Prepare the grid strips.** Make a copy of the Grid Strip student sheet and cut out each individual strip. Tape a grid strip onto each inflated globe approximately along the longitude of your city. Leave your city visible. Make sure you align the latitudes on the strip correctly with the corresponding latitudes on the globe and have the strip extend from the North Pole to the South Pole.

e. **With a permanent red pen, put a prominent dot on each grid strip at the latitude of your school.** Make another dot in the Southern Hemisphere at the same latitude south.

4. **Make a sunlight mask for each globe.** For each mask, follow the steps below:

   a. **Starting at one end of a drinking straw, cut a slit about half an inch long.** Insert the slit end of the straw into another drinking straw and tape them together to create a rod just over 15" long. This will be the upright "spine" for the sunlight mask.

   b. **Copy the Sunlight Mask Template.** Make two copies of the Sunlight Mask Template student sheet onto blank transparency acetate and then cut each piece of acetate into strips. For each mask, tape two strips together and overlap them as necessary to form a 17"-long strip. Do not block any of the clear squares with tape and make sure the squares in the overlapped portion of the strip are lined up and spaced evenly.

   c. **Tape the edge of the long strip to the straw rod.** Allow about 2" of excess transparency to extend past one end of the straw rod. This transparency "tail" will sit on the table at the bottom of the sunlight mask.

   d. **Clip a large binder clip to the bottom end of the sunlight mask to act as a stand.** Attach the clip at an angle so that it forms a stable tripod for holding up the sunlight mask. Adjust the sunlight mask so that it stands up from its base.

   e. **Crease the excess transparency tail at the bottom of the straw, where it touches the table.** This excess transparency tail can be taped down to make sure the sunlight mask stays in place once everything is set up correctly.

TEACHER CONSIDERATIONS

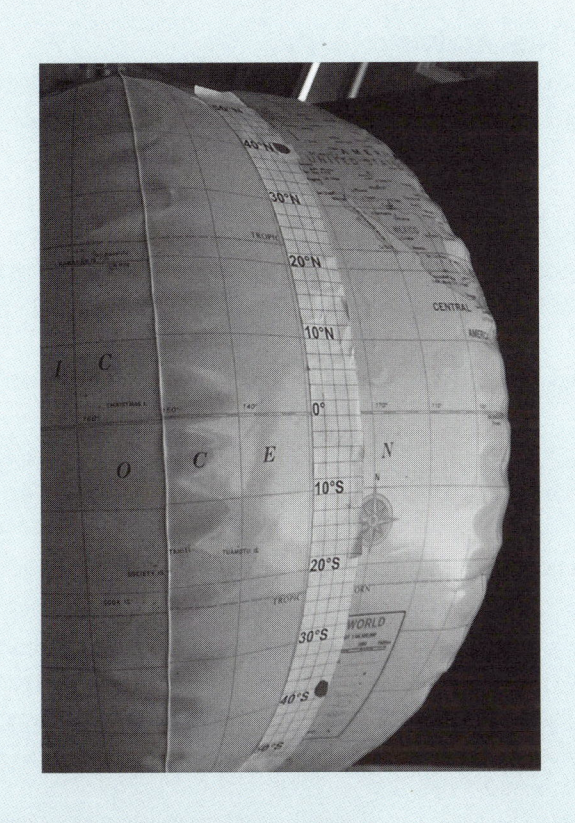

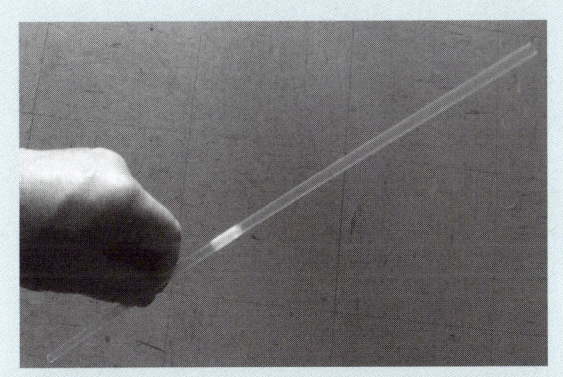

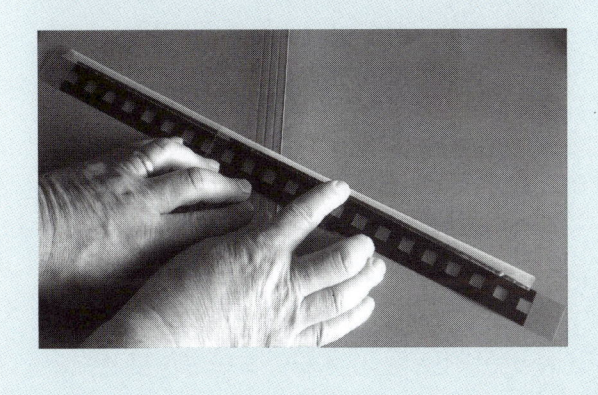

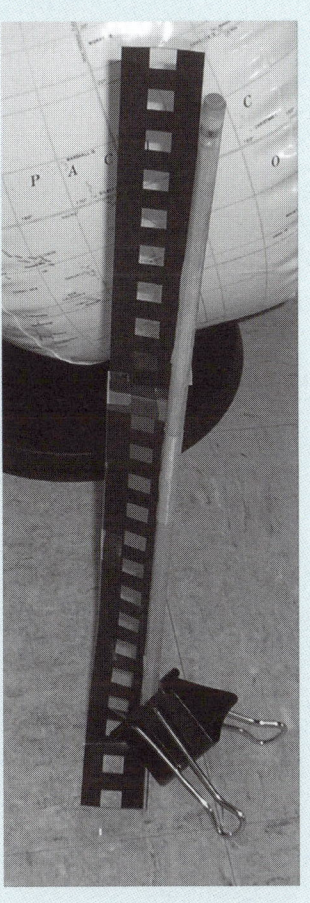

UNIT 2 • 339

SESSION 2.5   Intensity of Sunlight

On the Day of the Activity

1. **Prepare the key concept sheets.** Make a copy of each key concept and have them ready to post onto the classroom concept wall during the session.

2. **Post the Large Grid mini-poster.** Tape the grid onto a wall where it will be visible to the whole class. Alternatively, you can have a student volunteer hold up the grid for the demonstration.

3. Make a copy of the Observing Light Intensity student sheet for each student.

4. Decide how you will divide the class into teams of 3–4.

5. **Post the Polaris and A, B, C, D mini-posters.** If you removed these mini-posters after completing Session 2.4, tape them up again for this activity. As in Session 2.4, tape the Polaris mini-poster high in the center of one wall, and post the A mini-poster below it. Post the B, C, and D mini-posters on the other three walls, going counterclockwise around the room.

6. **Arrange desks or tables for stations near the mini-posters at each of the four walls.** Each wall will have one globe with two teams of three or four students working at each globe. Place one globe and one sunlight mask on each table.

7. **Set up the light in the center of the room.** Screw the light bulb into the socket and plug it in. Tape down the extension cord to prevent students from tripping over it. Check that all the globe stations are roughly the same distance away from the light bulb.

8. **Set up each Earth model.** Follow the steps below:

   a. **Tilt the globe stands toward Polaris.** The globe stands all have curved arms to hold the globe at just the proper tilt. Position the globes so that the North Poles of each are tilted toward the wall with the Polaris mini-poster. Remember that Polaris is very far away, so the direction of the tilts of all globes in the room should be parallel, toward the *wall*, but not directly at the sign.

   b. **Turn the globes so it is noontime on the white grid strip.** Keeping the globes tilted toward Polaris, rotate them within their stands until the white grid strip on each globe is facing the direction of the light-bulb "Sun."

TEACHER CONSIDERATIONS

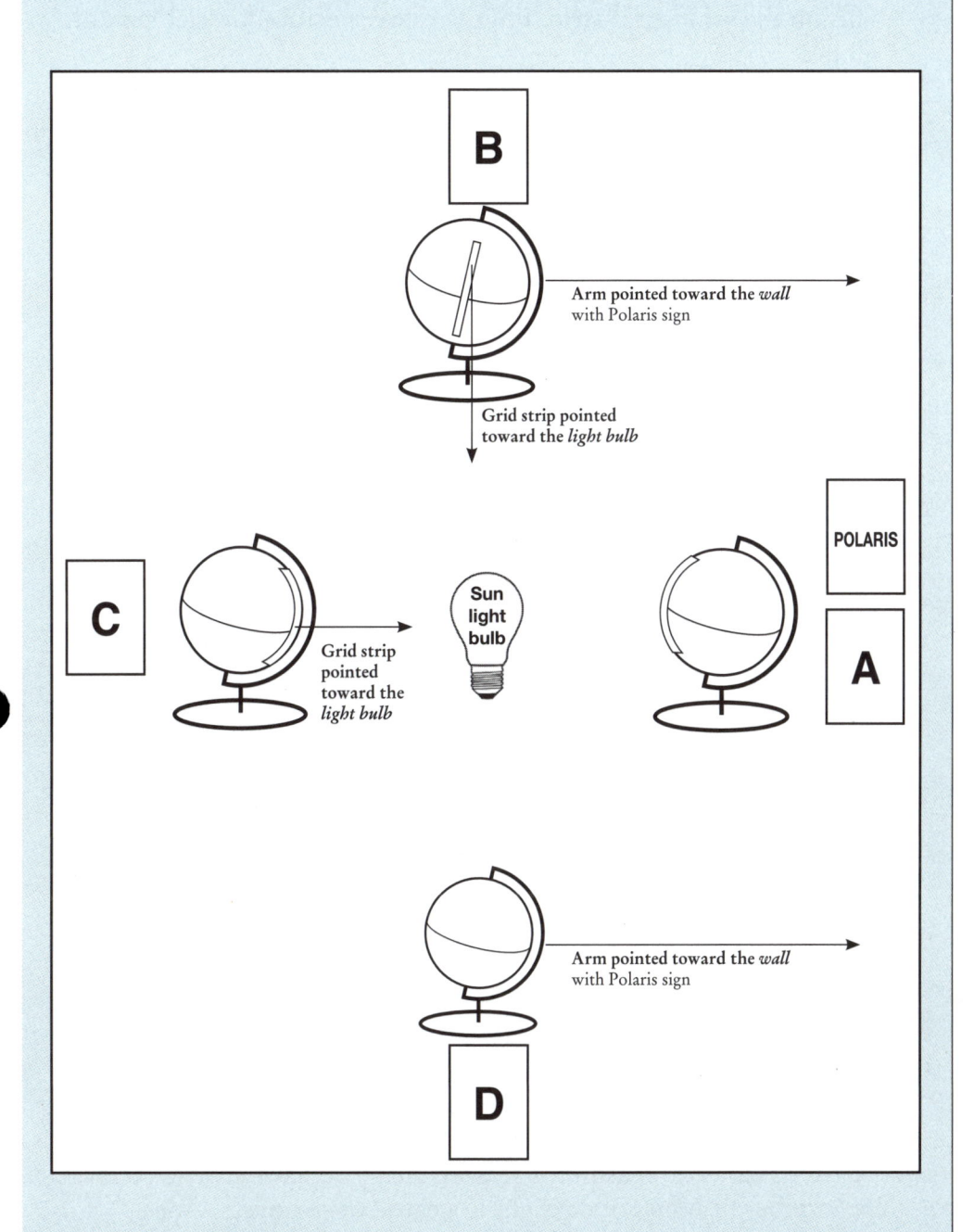

B

Arm pointed toward the *wall* with Polaris sign →

Grid strip pointed toward the *light bulb* ↓

C

Grid strip pointed toward the *light bulb* →

Sun light bulb

POLARIS

A

Arm pointed toward the *wall* with Polaris sign →

D

UNIT 2 • 341

SESSION 2.5 Intensity of Sunlight

Before the start of class, turn on the "Sun" and turn off the classroom lights. Check that each globe station has been set up correctly and that the white grid strips are visibly lit up.

c. Position a sunlight mask between each globe and the Sun. Turn on the light bulb, turn off the classroom lights, and position a sunlight mask in front of each globe so that the mask's shadow falls on the white grid strip. Follow these specifics for each pair of globes:

- **For globes at walls A and C:** The shadow of the sunlight mask should form a vertical line on the globe. It is important that the Earth globe is turned so that the white grid strip faces directly toward the Sun, and that the shadow of the sunlight mask falls in a vertical line on the white strip and does not curve to one side or the other. The sunlight mask and the globe should be about two finger widths apart.

- **For globes at walls B and D:** With the white grid strip facing the Sun, line up the sunlight mask so that it is two finger widths from the globe. Notice that at walls B and D, in order to get the shadow of the sunlight mask to fall on the white grid strip on the globe, you need to tilt the sunlight masks in their stands by 23.5 degrees to match the tilt of Earth.

GO! Investigating Light Intensity

1. **Review that the number of hours of daylight is a reason for seasons.** Have your students think back to the two Earth models (one with a tilt and one without) they observed during the last session. Ask, "What is a real reason for seasons that you have learned so far?" [The number of hours of daylight is a cause of seasons.]

2. **Considering intensity of sunlight.** Explain to the class that although the number of hours of daylight is indeed one key cause of seasons, there is one more issue they need to investigate to conclude their study of seasons: how the *intensity* of sunlight changes as Earth orbits the Sun.

TEACHER CONSIDERATIONS

PROVIDING MORE EXPERIENCE
Using Pencils To Model Light Rays

Another way to represent how light is less concentrated when striking the ground at a shallow angle is to use pencils to model light rays. Take several pencils and have students imagine that each pencil is a bundle of light rays. Hold the pencils together and touch them to the paper so that they are perpendicular to the paper, representing the steepest possible Sun angle. Wiggle the pencils so they leave marks on the paper. Next, hold the pencils so they touch the paper at a very oblique angle, sliding each pencil along the other until the tips touch the paper as shown. Wiggle the pencils again to make marks on the paper. These marks are farther apart, representing a lesser concentration of sunlight. Students can repeat this with pencils and scrap paper.

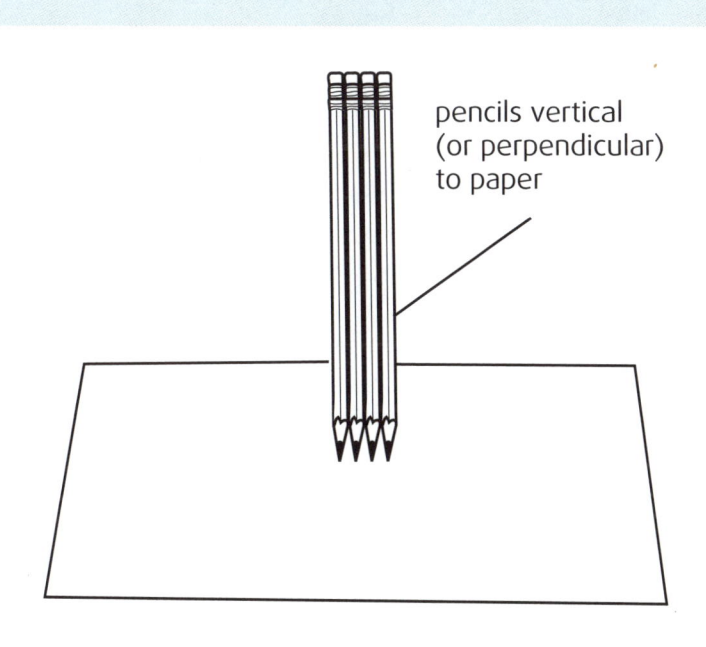

pencils vertical (or perpendicular) to paper

pencils at a very oblique angle or nearly parallel to paper

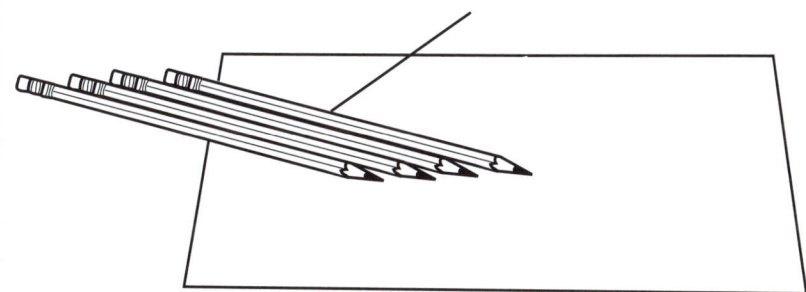

SESSION 2.5 Intensity of Sunlight

3. **Demonstrate light intensity.** Shine the flashlight on the posted Large Grid mini-poster. Hold the flashlight perpendicular to the grid and far enough away from it so that the light fills only one square on the grid. Tell students that the intensity of light on the paper has to do with how bright the light appears on the paper. Say that *light intensity* means how *concentrated* the light energy is in any one place.

4. **Ways to change the intensity of light.** Ask the class, "How can I change the intensity of light on the paper?" [Change the distance between the flashlight and the paper or change the angle at which the light strikes the paper.]

5. **Show how increasing the distance between the flashlight and the grid decreases light intensity.** Pull the flashlight back from the grid until the light fills about four squares on the grid. Ask, "What's happened to the intensity of the light on the paper?" [It's decreased. The light fills more space but looks less concentrated, or dimmer.] Point out that the flashlight is still putting out the same amount of light—but now the light that was concentrated on one square has spread out over four squares.

6. **Show how changing the angle of the light also decreases light intensity.** Move the flashlight closer to the grid again so that it fills only one square. Without changing the distance between the flashlight and the paper, tilt the flashlight slightly to one side until the light fills two squares. Ask students whether the light intensity has increased or decreased. [Decreased.] Explain that you changed the angle of the light hitting the grid by moving the flashlight from a steep angle (nearly perpendicular to the grid) to a shallow one (almost parallel to the wall with the light striking the grid from the side).

7. **Considering whether changes in light intensity are related to seasons.** Tell the class that they have just seen two different ways (distance and angle) in which the same amount of light could be made to shine onto a piece of paper with different intensities. Ask if the changing distance between the Sun and Earth might affect the light intensity of sunlight reaching Earth. [Not significantly.] Ask, "Do you think the angle of the sunlight reaching Earth might cause changes that are related to the seasons?" Accept all answers and tell the class that they will be investigating this further today.

Preparing to Observe and Record Data

1. **Introduce today's model.** Explain to the class that they will be using another model today to study the intensity of sunlight reaching Earth. Say that this model is similar to last session's models in many ways: a light bulb will represent the Sun, the mini-posters on the wall will represent four different positions in Earth's orbit, and Earth's spin axis will point toward Polaris.

If your students struggle with this question about the changing distance, remind them of the football-field model from Session 2.1. Earth's orbit is nearly circular, and the changes in Sun-Earth distance are so small, that a changing distance between Earth and the Sun doesn't significantly affect the intensity of sunlight.

TEACHER CONSIDERATIONS

SCIENCE NOTES

The fact that doubling the flashlight distance decreases light intensity by a factor of four is a manifestation of the inverse square law of light intensity, which states that intensity of light is inversely proportional to the square of the distance from the light source. Twice the distance yields ¼ the intensity, three times the distance yields ⅑ the intensity, and so on. In general:

$$I = \frac{K}{r^2}$$

I = intensity, r = distance, and K is a constant

It can be very tricky deciding what terms to use to describe the angle at which light strikes the ground. You may have heard the terms *indirect light* and *direct light*, but these terms are often used to describe light that has either reflected off another object, such as indirect lighting in a room. For this reason, we do not recommend using the terms *direct* and *indirect light* in the context of trying to describe angles of light rays. We recommend that you decide on terms to use and be consistent in their use. For light that is nearly perpendicular to the surface it strikes, the term *steep angle* can be good, as long as it is first associated with the idea of light rays nearly perpendicular to the surface. For light rays that are nearly parallel to the surface they strike, the term *shallow angle* could be appropriate, as long as it is first associated with the idea of light rays nearly parallel to the surface.

Steep angle: Rays more perpendicular to the surface. The angle between the horizon and the Sun's sky position is steep or large.

Shallow angle: Rays more parallel to the surface. The angle between the horizon and the Sun's sky position is shallow or small.

One teacher said, "The students were surprised at how intense light could become by 'concentrating' its beam."

SESSION 2.5   Intensity of Sunlight

Name:_____

Observing Light Intensity

Earth's Orbit Position	Number of squares lit ___° North	Number of squares lit ___° South
A		
B		
C		
D		

2. **Review seasons in the Northern Hemisphere for different positions in Earth's orbit.** Ask students what seasons and day lengths they observed for the Northern Hemisphere in each part of Earth's orbit: A, B, C, and D. [Near A, it is winter solstice in the Northern Hemisphere and day lengths are short. Near C, it is summer solstice in the Northern Hemisphere and day lengths are long. Near B it is spring equinox in the Northern Hemisphere; near D it is fall equinox. The day lengths at B and D are about equal.]

3. **Looking at Earth in its different seasonal orbit positions.** Point out the Earth globes set up near each wall mini-poster and remind students that the globes represent Earth at four seasonal places (A, B, C, and D) in its orbit around the Sun.

4. **Observing light intensity using grid strips on the Earth globes.** Hold up one globe and point out the white grid strip attached to it. Tell the class that this grid is like the posted Large Grid they were looking at earlier in the flashlight demonstration. The white grid strip on the globe will allow them to gauge the intensity of light coming from the light-bulb "Sun."

5. **Pass out the Observing Light Intensity student sheets.** Tell students they will be observing the light intensity for two different places on the globes at each of the four seasonal orbit positions.

6. **Point out the two locations on the globe for measuring light intensity.** On the student sheet, point out the first row of the data table and tell students they will measure light intensity on the four globes for two different locations. Say that one location is in the Northern Hemisphere at the latitude of their city and the other is at the same latitude in the Southern Hemisphere. Both locations are marked in red pen on the white grid strip. Using one of the globes, point out these locations to the class. Have students put the degrees of latitude number on the blank line of their student sheets.

7. **Remind the class of the earlier flashlight demonstration.** Ask, "In which case was the light more intense—when it filled just one square or when it was spread out over several squares?" [When it filled just one square.] Explain that, similarly, light intensity on the globes can be measured by counting how many boxes on the white grid strip are filled by a square beam of light coming from the model Sun.

TEACHER CONSIDERATIONS

SESSION 2.5 Intensity of Sunlight

8. **Explain how to measure light intensity on the globes.** Tell students to make a measurement for the square beam of light that falls closest to the red mark in the Northern Hemisphere and another measurement for the square beam of light that falls closest to the red mark in the Southern Hemisphere. Say that to do this, students should count how many boxes on the grid strip are lit up by the square beam of light from the model Sun. Partially lit boxes should be estimated as approximate fractions of a box. Students should record their results on the student sheet with the corresponding latitude and Earth-orbit position.

9. **Students will work in teams.** Tell students they will be making their observations as a group, but each person needs to record his or her own data onto their Observing Light Intensity student sheet.

10. **Teams will move from globe to globe.** Tell teams they will observe one globe at a time. Teammates should help one another gather data. Teams will start at one orbit position and move to a globe at another position until they've looked at all four globes.

11. **Students should work cooperatively.** Say that since there is only one globe at each wall position, students will need to work cooperatively with one another to take their measurements. Emphasize that, above all, students should avoid blocking the light from the model Sun, and that they should not touch the globes or the sunlight masks. Students observing in front should crouch down so others behind them will be able to see.

12. **Summarize what students will be doing.** Remind students that they will:

    a. **Observe one globe at a time with their team.** Let the class know if you will be signaling for them to move to the next globe, or whether they will be allowed to move at their own pace.

    b. **Measure the light intensity of the location (marked in red) in the Northern Hemisphere.** They should count the number of boxes on the white grid strip that are lit up by one square beam of light coming from the model Sun and record the number on their student sheets.

    c. **Measure the light intensity of the location at the same latitude (marked in red) in the Southern Hemisphere.** After students count the number of boxes on the grid strip that are lit up, they should record the number on their student sheets.

    d. **Teams should make two light-intensity measurements for all four orbit positions: A, B, C, and D.**

TEACHER CONSIDERATIONS

SESSION 2.5   Intensity of Sunlight

Making Observations

1. **Divide the class into teams of 3–4.** Assign two teams to each of the globes to start with. (If you decided to use eight stations, then assign one team per station.) Have students move to their stations. Remind everyone to cooperate and share the globes.

2. **Teams make their measurements.** Turn on the light-bulb "Sun" and then turn off the classroom lights. Have students make their light-intensity measurements. Circulate from globe to globe, reminding students to count the number of boxes on the white grid strip lit by one square beam of light from the model Sun. As you circulate, check globes to make sure that they remain properly aligned. Either signal teams to move to the next globe or have teams move around the room at their own rate. When everyone has made their measurements at each of the four orbit positions, turn the room lights back on and ask students to return to their seats.

Discussing the Data

1. **Help students interpret their data.** Ask some preliminary focusing questions, such as, "Is the light intensity more or less if several squares on the grid strip were lit up?" [Less.] "When the light was spread out more, was the light brighter or dimmer?" [Dimmer.] "Is the light intensity more or less if only a few squares on the grid strip were lit up?" [More.] "When the light was concentrated in fewer squares, was the light brighter or dimmer?" [Brighter.]

2. **Share results for orbit position A.** Have teams report their numbers for orbit position A. This can be done by having one team report their number for the Northern Hemisphere location in orbit position A and then ask for a show of hands from the class to see: how many agreed exactly with that number, how many counted fewer squares, and how many counted more squares. Then ask another team to report their number for the Southern Hemisphere location in orbit position A, again asking for a show of hands from the class to compare results. Another possibility would be to copy the data table onto the chalkboard and ask teams to record their data on the class table. From this, you (or the class) can calculate an average light intensity for each of the latitude locations—for all four orbit positions.

TEACHER CONSIDERATIONS

SESSION 2.5 Intensity of Sunlight

3. **The difference in light intensity between Northern and Southern Hemispheres.** Ask, "When Earth is near wall A, which hemisphere had more intense sunlight—Northern or Southern?" [Southern.] Ask, "In which hemisphere would it be summer solstice?" [Southern.] Ask, "Which season would be beginning in the Northern Hemisphere?" [Winter.] Allow students to make sense of this. Ask next, "Does it make sense for it to be summer where the light intensity is highest?" "Why?" [Allow students a little time to draw the connection for themselves. In short, yes, it does make sense. When the light intensity is higher, the sunlight is not only brighter, but it also heats up the ground more. When the light intensity is low, the light is dimmer, and it heats up the ground less.]

4. **The angle of the sunlight hitting the ground and the position of the Sun in the sky at orbit position A.** Ask students whether the Sun would appear high or low in the sky at noon in the Northern Hemisphere when Earth is near wall A. [The Sun would appear low in the sky, since the light comes in at a shallow angle and is less intense.]

5. **Share results for orbit position B.** Have teams share their results for Earth orbit position B. Gather the class results the same way as before. Ask, "Which hemisphere had more intense sunlight—Northern or Southern?" [There was roughly no difference in light intensity between the Northern and Southern Hemispheres.] Ask, "What season is about to begin in the Northern Hemisphere?" [Students may struggle with this a bit. You may have to remind them that Earth orbits the Sun counterclockwise as seen from above. If it was winter solstice in position A, students should be able to conclude that it is spring equinox in position B, and that the spring season is beginning.]

6. **Share results for orbit position C.** Have teams share their results for Earth orbit position C. Ask, "Which hemisphere had more intense sunlight—Northern or Southern?" [Northern.] Ask, "Which season is beginning in the Northern Hemisphere?" [Summer.] Ask, "And in the Southern Hemisphere?" [Winter.] Ask, "How does this compare to when Earth was in orbit position A?" [The results are opposite.]

7. **The angle of the sunlight hitting the ground and the position of the Sun in the sky at orbit position C.** Ask students whether the Sun would appear high or low in the sky at noon in the Northern Hemisphere when Earth is near wall C. [It would appear high in the sky, with its light coming down almost from straight above.] If students have trouble visualizing the position of the Sun, go back and forth between positions A and C and help them see the difference.

TEACHER CONSIDERATIONS

SESSION 2.5 Intensity of Sunlight

8. **Share results for orbit position D.** Have teams share their results. You can ask the same questions as you did for orbit position B. The light intensity should be similar between the Northern and Southern Hemispheres. Ask what season would be beginning in the Northern Hemisphere at position D. [Fall.] Have your students compare these results to the results from orbit position B. They should be similar.

9. **Help your students draw connections between the angle of the sunlight hitting the ground, light intensity on the ground, and seasons.** For example, you could say, "We observed that light intensity is different between the Northern and Southern Hemispheres when Earth is in orbit position A. At position A, the light intensity in the Northern Hemisphere is *less* than it is in the Southern Hemisphere. It is winter solstice for us here in the Northern Hemisphere. In which hemisphere is the light hitting the ground at a steep angle (close to straight up and down)?" [Southern.] Ask, "In which hemisphere is the light hitting the ground at a shallow angle (coming in from the side)?" [Northern.] Ask, "Is the angle that light hits the ground important for seasons?" [Yes. That's what makes the light intensity different in the Northern and Southern Hemispheres.] Post on the concept wall, under Key Space Science Concepts:

   At the beginning of summer, sunlight falls at a steep angle and shines most intensely on Earth's surface.

   At the beginning of winter, sunlight falls at a shallow angle and shines least intensely on Earth's surface.

10. **Recall how the tilt of Earth affected amount of daylight hours during the day.** Say, "In the Northern Hemisphere's winter—when the Earth is in position A—we have seen that the light is less intense on the ground." Ask, "From the model in the previous session, is this the time when days are longer or shorter?" [Shorter.] Note that both effects—shorter daylight hours and less intense sunlight—help make winter. Similarly, both of the two opposite effects—longer daylight hours and more intense sunlight—help make summer. Remind students of the posted key concept from Session 2.4:

    Earth's tilted spin axis causes seasonal changes in hours of daylight and night throughout the year.

TEACHER CONSIDERATIONS

SESSION 2.5   Intensity of Sunlight

11. **Consider Earth with an untilted spin axis.** Ask, "Why is there a difference in the angle that sunlight hits the ground in the Northern and Southern Hemispheres?" [Students may debate this for a while. The reason is the tilt of Earth.] Go on to ask, "What do you think would happen if Earth was not tilted? For instance, what if the globe at orbit position A had its axis pointed straight up instead of toward Polaris?" Hold a globe from position A so that the spin axis is pointed toward the ceiling, perpendicular to the light from the model Sun. Ask, "Would there be any difference in the *angle* that sunlight hits the cities marked in red in the Northern and Southern Hemispheres?" [No.] "Would there be any difference in the *light intensity*?" [No.] "Would there be any difference in *day length*?" [No.] "So if Earth was not tilted, would there be seasons?" [No.] Students may have to think hard about this question, and it may open a discussion that reveals any lingering misconceptions they have. Allow students to share openly, without correcting them. Most of these misconceptions will be reviewed and corrected during the evidence circles in the final session.

12. **Revisit Questions #3, #5, and #6 on the Pre-unit 2 Questionnaire.** Show the Pre-unit 2 Questionnaire transparencies. Ask students how they might answer Questions #3, #5, and #6 now, and why.

13. **Collect student work.** Collect each student's Observing Light Intensity student sheet and place them into their student folders.

TEACHER CONSIDERATIONS

QUESTIONNAIRE CONNECTION

Questionnaire Connections allows you to assess your students' understanding of key unit concepts through the discussion of questions on the Pre-unit 2 Questionnaire. **Do not give out the correct responses to your students**. Instead, ask them to consider the questions, and whether they would change their answers (and why) based on what they have just learned. Additional information to help you interpret your students' responses to the questions can be found in the About the Pre-unit 2 Questionnaire Responses on page 275.

SESSION 2.6
The Reasons for Seasons

Overview
In the video, *A Private Universe*, graduating students from Harvard are interviewed about what they think causes the seasons. The students confidently respond with incorrect responses based on their own misconceptions. You may find it useful to show this video to your students at the end of this unit, so they can see how far they have come in their understanding of seasons. In this session, equipped with understandings gained from all of their investigations in this unit, students work again in evidence circles to use their newly acquired knowledge to debate three explanations for the seasons. This final session gives students an opportunity to internalize and deepen their new understanding of what causes the seasons: that Earth is a spinning globe whose axis is tilted with respect to its orbit around the Sun, and that this gives rise to: (a) a varying number of daylight hours in different seasons and (b) variations in the intensity of sunlight on the ground related to the angle at which the light strikes the ground. There are no new key concepts for this session.

The Reasons for Seasons	Estimated Time
Evidence Circles	30 minutes
Taking the Post-unit 2 Questionnaire	15 minutes
Total	**45 minutes**

What You Need
For the class:
- ❑ (optional) a TV connected to a VHS or DVD player
- ❑ (optional) 1 copy of the video, *A Private Universe*

For each student:
- ❑ 1 copy of the Three Explanations for Seasons student sheet from the copymaster packet or CD-ROM file
- ❑ 1 copy of the Post-unit 2 Questionnaire (five pages) from the copymaster packet or CD-ROM file
- ❑ student folder with unit work (from Session 2.1)
- ❑ (optional) 1 copy of the A Private Universe—Student Reading from the copymaster packet or CD-ROM file
- ❑ (optional) 1 copy of the Seasons on Mars—Student Reading from the copymaster packet or CD-ROM file

Getting Ready
1. Decide how you will divide the class into teams of three for the evidence-circle activity.

Unit Goals
The seasons are not caused by variations in Earth's distance from the Sun.

Earth's spin axis remains tilted toward Polaris as it orbits the Sun.

Earth's tilt does not significantly change its distance from the Sun.

Seasons are caused by Earth's tilt, which affects the intensity of sunlight and the number of daylight hours at different locations on Earth.

TEACHER CONSIDERATIONS

TEACHING NOTES
Please see the Resources and References section on page 59 for more information about obtaining a copy of the video, *A Private Universe*. (Educators can obtain a free copy of the DVD.)

Although both the A Private Universe—Student Reading and Seasons on Mars—Student Reading are optional, they are highly recommended if you have the time.

Key Vocabulary

Scientific Inquiry Vocabulary

Evidence
Model
Observation
Prediction
Scale
Scale model
Scientific explanation

Space Science Vocabulary

Equator
Equinox
Hemisphere
Intensity
Latitude
Orbit
Solstice
Spin axis

SESSION 2.6   The Reasons for Seasons

2. **Make copies of student sheets.** For each student, make one copy of the Three Explanations for Seasons student sheet (one page) and one copy of the Post-unit 2 Questionnaire (five pages).

3. **Prepare student folders with unit work.** Check that all student work for the unit has been put into the folders and be prepared to hand them out during the session.

4. **Optional: Copy the student reading(s).** If you plan to have your students read either A Private Universe—Student Reading or Seasons on Mars—Student Reading (or both), make copies for each student.

5. **Optional: Set up the TV and VHS or DVD player.** If you plan to show *A Private Universe*, connect the VHS or DVD player to the TV and pause the video at the beginning of the seasons section.

GO! Evidence Circles

1. **Time to make sense of it all.** Remind the class that they have been gathering evidence about what causes seasons, and you would like them to have some time to discuss and think about all this evidence and what it means. Remind them that they already know more about what causes seasons than many adults!

2. **Reintroduce evidence circles.** Explain to the class that they will work in evidence circles in groups of three. Hold up a copy of the Three Explanations for Seasons student sheets, and say that on the sheet are three statements about why seasons occur. Tell them these three statements may or may not be correct. Evidence-circle groups will discuss the statements using what they have learned in this unit as evidence to support their ideas. Remind the class of the posted key concept from Session 2.2:

   Scientific explanations are based on evidence gathered from observations and investigations.

3. **Explain the procedure.** Tell students they should use the following procedure to discuss each statement: First, one student will read Statement #1 aloud, and then everyone will say if they agree or disagree with the statement, ***giving evidence for why they agree or disagree***. Different students should read Statements #2 and #3, and the group should follow the same procedure in discussing these statements. Everyone should write on their Three Explanations for Seasons student sheets whether they agree or disagree with each statement, and they should also write down the evidence that backs up their thinking.

360 • SPACE SCIENCE SEQUENCE 6-8   Session 2.6: The Reasons for Seasons

TEACHER CONSIDERATIONS

ASSESSMENT OPPORTUNITY
EMBEDDED ASSESSMENT: EVIDENCE-CIRCLE RESPONSES: THREE EXPLANATIONS FOR SEASONS
The Three Explanations for Seasons student sheets, which students complete in evidence circles, can be used as an embedded assessment. Please see the scoring guide on page 108 in the Assessment section.

SESSION 2.6 The Reasons for Seasons

4. **Model the procedure with the whole class.** Write the following sample statement on the board and use it to model the procedure. (This is not one of the statements on the student sheet.)

   Seasons happen because Earth's tilt makes us closer to the Sun in the summer and farther away from it in the winter.

   a. **Have one student read the sample statement aloud to the class.**

   b. **Ask a few students to say if they agree or disagree and to explain why.** During the discussion, listen and help students apply evidence to support their arguments. If no one mentions it, remind students of the scale-model activity from Session 2.2. Ask how the scale model can be used as evidence to argue against this statement.

   c. **Help students to write a sample answer.** Ask students how they might write an answer to this statement. [The scale model is evidence that Earth is so far away from the Sun that even tilting it doesn't make any part of it closer to the Sun by much. The distance to the Sun is still huge, compared to the size of Earth.]

   d. **Reach a final conclusion about this statement.** Ask the class if they would agree or disagree with the statement, given all the evidence they have discussed. [Disagree.] Conclude by saying that someone who thinks this statement is correct must not understand how far Earth is from the Sun.

5. **Pass out student folders with unit work.** Pass out the student folders and suggest that students use their collected work from the unit, along with all the key concepts on the wall, to look for evidence to support their answers.

6. **Divide the class into teams of three.** Pass out a Three Explanations for Seasons student sheet to each student.

TEACHER CONSIDERATIONS

SESSION 2.6   The Reasons for Seasons

7. Groups begin discussing statements. Circulate around the room to assist students with their reasoning and writing. As students share their thinking with one another, you can confirm (as the issue arises) that both Statements #2 and #3 are supported by evidence. After about 15 minutes, regain the attention of the entire class.

8. Class discussion of statements and evidence. Help students apply evidence to support or refute the three statements:

Statement #1: In summer, Earth is closer to the Sun. In winter, Earth is farther from the Sun.

Disagree. Evidence: In the football-field model, we found evidence that Earth's orbit is almost circular, and the Sun is in the middle of Earth's orbit. We also learned that Earth is actually a bit closer to the Sun in January each year. The graphs of temperatures and day lengths also showed that not all locations on Earth have summer (or winter) at the same time—this is evidence that Earth can't be significantly closer or farther from the Sun at any time during the year.

Statement #2: In summer, the Northern Hemisphere is tilted toward the Sun. This tilt causes us to have more hours of daylight in the summer.

Agree. Evidence: When we held the model Earth spheres around the light-bulb Sun, we observed that day length does change according to Earth's tilt. When the North Pole is tilted toward the Sun, the day length there is so long that, on some days, the Sun never sets! Other places in the Northern Hemisphere had longer day lengths around the time of the summer solstice as well. Longer day lengths mean more light and warmth from the Sun, which is what causes summer.

Statement #3: In summer, the Northern Hemisphere is tilted toward the Sun. This tilt makes sunlight more intense in summer.

Agree. Evidence: We observed that a flashlight's beam was brighter (and more intense) when the light beam hit the paper at a steeper angle and when it covered fewer squares on the grid. In the activity with the light-bulb Sun and Earth globes, the light hitting Earth was more intense at the summer solstice, when Earth's tilt made the light hit the ground at a steep angle. This evidence explains why we have more intense light as we begin summer, which warms Earth more than less intense light does.

TEACHER CONSIDERATIONS

SESSION 2.6 The Reasons for Seasons

**Post-unit 2 Questionnaire:
Why Are There Seasons?**

Name:_____

1. These two pictures show the same tree on two different days at noon. Why do the Sun's rays come in at different angles? Explain why this occurs.

_____
_____
_____
_____
_____

A   B

Taking the Post-unit 2 Questionnaire

1. **Remind students of the Pre-unit 2 Questionnaire they took at the beginning of the unit.** Ask, "Do you think you'd like to change any of your answers on the Pre-unit 2 Questionnaire?" Tell students they have learned a lot about what causes seasons, and now they will be able to fill out the questionnaire again using the evidence they have gathered during the unit.

2. **Pass out the Post-unit 2 Questionnaire and have students begin.** Tell students they should feel free to refer to the concept wall and their student folders. Give the class about 10 minutes to work on their questionnaires.

3. **Discuss the questionnaire as a class.** Have students hold on to their questionnaires and take a few minutes to have a class discussion about the questions. Encourage students to compare their Post-unit 2 Questionnaire responses with their Pre-unit 2 Questionnaire responses.

4. **Students as seasons experts.** Praise your students for their excellent scientific work throughout the unit and the leaps they've made in understanding. Congratulate them on becoming seasons experts!

5. **Optional: Pass out the student reading(s).**

6. **Optional: Show the class the video, *A Private Universe*.** The video covers several topics—show your students only the section about seasons.

A Private Universe—Student Reading

Name:_____

If you understand what causes Earth to have different seasons, you should be very proud! Most college students, adults, and even teachers don't really understand what causes seasons. This was clearly seen when a team of researchers went out to ask people about the reason for seasons.

Researchers first went to the graduation ceremonies at Harvard University. They interviewed 23 graduates and professors about what causes seasons, and only two knew the right answer! Most thought that Earth was warmer in the summer because it was closer to the Sun and colder in the winter because it was farther away. Many of these people had taken advanced science courses in high school, and some of them had even majored in science at Harvard. It seemed that no matter how much or how little science they had studied, their answers were the same.

The researchers then went to a ninth-grade classroom to see if students would give the same answers as Harvard graduates and professors. They found that most students did give the same answer—that distance from the Sun was the explanation for the seasons.

After the interview, the ninth-grade students had a class lesson on the movement of Earth and the real reason for seasons. The students were interviewed again after the lesson to see if their ideas had changed. Some ideas did change, but not all.

One of the best students in the class learned that Earth's orbit is very close to a circle, so she understood that it wasn't changes in distance that cause the seasons. She also knew that the tilt of Earth on its axis causes our seasons. She understood that when the Northern Hemisphere is tilted toward the Sun, it is summer there. However, she still held on to some mistaken ideas about seasons.

When the researchers asked this student to explain further, she said that the light was weaker in winter because it had to "bounce off" something to get to Earth. Her reason was not correct, but it made sense to her. Like many of us, she had come up with her own private reason for how a tilted Earth could lead to seasons.

The student they interviewed probably didn't understand that a steeper angle of light makes the light more intense. Maybe it would have helped her if she was able to experiment with light herself to see that the intensity of light changes with different angles. If she had some evidence about light angles and intensity, she might revise her thinking about what causes seasons. Learning the real reasons why light affects seasons might help her give up her private explanation about bouncing light.

What is the best way to help people understand the real reasons for seasons? The researchers suggest that we need to find out what they really think, and then give them the evidence they need to change their minds.

Seasons on Mars—Student Reading

Name:_____

People have a lot of questions about the planet Mars. No astronauts have gone there yet, but one day we hope they will. Several NASA missions have explored Mars, including the Mars Exploration Rovers. The two rovers, named "Spirit" and "Opportunity," have been exploring the Red Planet for over one full Martian year! Since Mars travels around the Sun more slowly than Earth does, and its orbit is much bigger, a Mars year is about twice as long as an Earth year. During their time on Mars, the rovers have gathered amazing new evidence about the Red Planet, including what it is like there in different seasons.

What Causes Seasons on Mars?

One of the reasons for seasons on Mars is the same as on Earth—the tilt of the planet's axis. Mars' tilt is slightly more than Earth's. As on Earth, this makes parts of Mars face the Sun more directly at times. When the Sun's light hits those parts at a steeper angle, the light intensity is greater, and so it is warmer. The planet's tilt also causes those places to have longer daylight.

But seasons on Mars have an added cause that we don't have on Earth. Earth's orbit around the Sun is almost a circle, so the difference in our distance to the Sun at different times is very small compared to the total distance from Earth to the Sun. But the orbit of Mars is not a circle. It is much more stretched out. The distance between Mars and the Sun varies by almost 42 million kilometers. That distance does make a difference in the temperature!

Comparing the Orbits of Earth and Mars

Mars moves faster in its orbit when it is closer to the Sun and slower when it is far from the Sun, which means the seasons have different lengths on Mars. On Earth, the seasons are about equal.

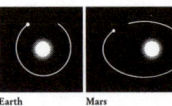

Earth   Mars

Seasons (Northern Hemisphere)	Earth (in days)	Mars (in Earth days)
Spring	93	171
Summer	94	199
Fall	89	171
Winter	89	146

---

366 • SPACE SCIENCE SEQUENCE 6–8   Session 2.6: The Reasons for Seasons

TEACHER CONSIDERATIONS

TEACHING NOTES

It is up to you whether you would like to allow your students to keep their work folders with them as they complete the Post-unit 2 Questionnaire. Although it may seem counterintuitive to allow your students access to information while taking the questionnaire, we recommend that you allow them to refer to the key concepts and their unit work. Much like the evidence-circle activity, the questionnaire is an excellent opportunity for students to apply and conceptualize what they have learned.

PROVIDING MORE EXPERIENCE
Essays by Seasons Experts

1. **Students explain, in writing, why seasons occur.** Say that as a final proof of their expertise on seasons, students will write essays to explain why there are seasons. If you have had them view the video, *A Private Universe*, you may even suggest that they write a letter to the Harvard graduates who think that the reasons for seasons have to do with Earth's distance from the Sun! Encourage students to illustrate their essays using pictures, graphs, and/or diagrams.

2. **Student peer review of each others' essays.** Have students exchange, read, and constructively critique each others' essays.

Are there seasons on other planets? Explain that Earth's axis is tilted by 23.5° with respect to Earth's orbit around the Sun. Say that the spin axes of other planets have different tilt angles. Uranus' tilt angle, for example, is nearly 90°! Ask students what they think seasons might be like on Uranus. [Uranus probably has extremely hot summers and extremely cold winters.] Explain that most regions of the planet would experience midnight Sun for half the year and complete darkness for the other half of the year! Add that Uranus is actually a cold gas-giant planet, and that it is also very different from Earth in many other respects. (The question about seasons on Uranus could also serve as a revealing assessment question.) See the Background Information for Teachers, page 38 for more information.

For an excellent connection to the subject of seasons on other planets, see the Amazing Space website. One feature focuses on seasons on Neptune and the tilts of other planets and can be found at: http://amazing-space.stsci.edu/news/archive/2003/01

One teacher said, "Students enjoyed the two optional readings. They liked knowing that they know more than some Harvard graduates. They also learned interesting facts about Mars and its seasons."

Another said, "I emphasized the 'Private Universe' video because it was a real learning experience. My students identified with the students in the video as they tried to draw the correct movement of the Earth in its orbit. This closely paralleled the optional activity in Session 2.2 and my students made this connection."

UNIT 2 • 367

OPTIONAL
Prerequisite Activities

Overview
In this optional session, three activities that can be used, depending on the needs of your class, to strengthen your students' understanding of (1) the shape of Earth, (2) how the spinning of Earth causes day and night, and (3) the shape of Earth's orbit. The first two activities are best presented before beginning Unit 2, while the third is a hands-on activity about ellipses that deepens and extends concepts introduced in Session 2.2. These activities reinforce foundational ideas, without which students cannot build an accurate understanding of what causes the seasons.

Prerequisite Activities	Estimated Time
Shape-of-Earth Survey	10 minutes

Shape-of-Earth Survey
Use this activity if you think your class needs to review the concept that Earth's shape is spherical.

What You Need
- ❏ an overhead projector
- ❏ transparency of the Shape-of-Earth Survey from the transparency packet or CD-ROM file
- ❏ 1 Earth globe

GO! Shape-of-Earth Survey

1. **Survey students on Earth's shape.** Show the Shape-of-Earth Survey transparency. Ask, "Which drawing best represents the shape of Earth?" [A.]

2. **Why Earth appears flat.** Hold up the Earth globe and ask, "If Earth is shaped like a ball, why does it look flat or hilly to us?" [We are very, very small compared to Earth, and we can only see a small part of it around us. The part that we do see appears flat or hilly.]

3. **Gravity defines "down" on Earth.** Point out Australia's location on the globe relative to the United States. Ask, "Why don't people living in Australia fall off Earth?" [Gravity pulls us all toward Earth's center, so everyone on Earth, regardless of their location, feels that Earth is "down" and the sky is "up."]

Unit Goals
The seasons are not caused by variations in Earth's distance from the Sun.

Earth's spin axis remains tilted toward Polaris as it orbits the Sun.

Earth's tilt does not significantly change its distance from the Sun.

Seasons are caused by Earth's tilt, which affects the intensity of sunlight and the number of daylight hours at different locations on Earth.

TEACHER CONSIDERATIONS

Shape-of-Earth Survey

Which drawing best shows the shape of Earth that we are sitting/standing on?

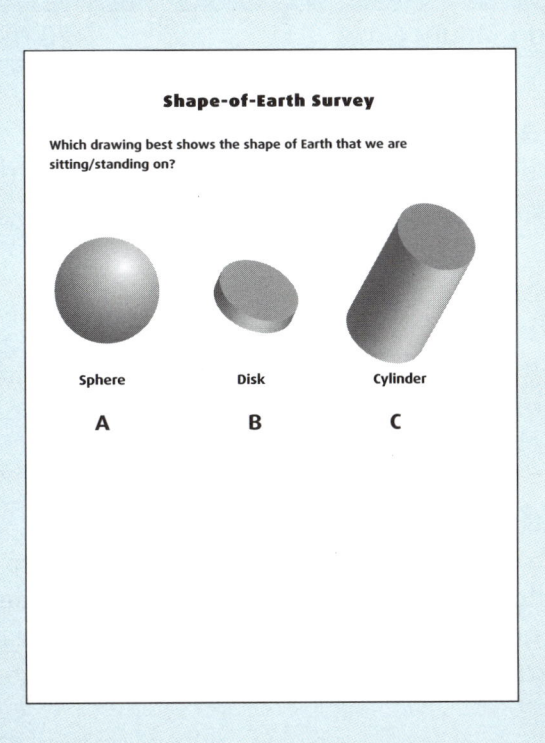

Sphere   Disk   Cylinder
A   B   C

Key Vocabulary

Scientific Inquiry Vocabulary

Evidence
Model
Observation
Prediction
Scale
Scale model
Scientific explanation

Space Science Vocabulary

Equator
Equinox
Hemisphere
Intensity
Latitude
Orbit
Solstice
Spin axis

UNIT 2 • 369

Optional Prerequisite Activities

Prerequisite Activities	Estimated Time
Night and Day on Mount Nose	20 minutes

Night and Day on Mount Nose

Use this activity if you think your class needs to review the concept that day and night are caused by the spinning of Earth.

What You Need

- ❏ 1 light bulb (any size or wattage)
- ❏ 1 clamp-on socket with no shade
- ❏ an extension cord
- ❏ 1 Earth globe

Getting Ready

Put the light bulb in the socket, plug it in, and clamp it to a table or chair in the middle of the room. Be sure that there is enough space around the light bulb for all students to gather in a circle around it. Tape the extension cord to the floor to prevent any students from tripping over it.

GO! Night and Day on Mount Nose

1. **Introduce the model.** Turn on the light bulb and turn off the room lights. Show the class the Earth globe and explain that an Earth-Sun model can be made with the light bulb as the Sun and the globe as Earth.

2. **How Earth moves.** Ask, "How does Earth move in relation to the Sun?" [Earth revolves around the Sun in an orbit. It also spins or rotates on its axis.] Show these two motions to the class or ask for one or more volunteers to demonstrate this. Ask students the following questions:

"How long does it take for Earth to orbit once around the Sun?" [One year.]

"How long does it take Earth to spin once on its axis?" [24 hours.]

"How many times does Earth spin around its axis during a year?" [365.]

TEACHER CONSIDERATIONS

Optional Prerequisite Activities

3. **Inaccuracies in this model.** Ask, "What does this model not accurately represent about the Sun-Earth model?" [It is not to scale. This model does not show the Sun's size or distance relative to Earth accurately.]

4. **Another model to observe night and day.** Gather students in a circle around the light bulb and tell them they will now use another model to understand what causes night and day. Say that the light bulb will still represent the Sun, but instead of a globe, each student will use his or her head to represent Earth. Have students imagine that their nose is a mountain, and that a person lives on the tip of their "Mount Nose." Say that the person is standing on the tip of Mount Nose, with his head pointing toward the light-bulb Sun. (A fun tip: One teacher had every student actually stand a tiny model person on the tips of their noses!)

5. **Noon on Mount Nose.** With the students facing the light bulb, ask, "For the person standing on your Mount Nose, where in the sky is the Sun?" [High in the sky, directly over the person's head.] Ask, "What time of day do you think it is for the person on Mount Nose?" [Noon.]

6. **Observing sunset.** Ask students to turn to their left and stop when their right ears are facing the Sun. Ask, "For the person on Mount Nose, where in the sky does the Sun now seem to be? [Near the horizon, low in the sky.] Ask, "What time of day is it now for the person on Mount Nose?" [Sunset.]

7. **Midnight on Mount Nose.** Have students continue to turn to their left until their backs are to the light bulb. Ask, "What time is it for the person on Mount Nose now?" [Around midnight.] Ask, "On what part of your head is it daytime?" [The back, because it is now facing the Sun.]

8. **Observing sunrise.** Have students make another quarter turn to the left so that their left ears are facing the Sun. Ask, "Where is the Sun in the sky now on Mount Nose?" [Low in the sky, just coming up.] Ask, "What time is it for the person on Mount Nose?" [Sunrise.] Have the class make another quarter turn to the left so that they are facing the light bulb.

9. **Additional time to observe night and day.** If time allows, give students the opportunity to rotate through several more days.

TEACHER CONSIDERATIONS

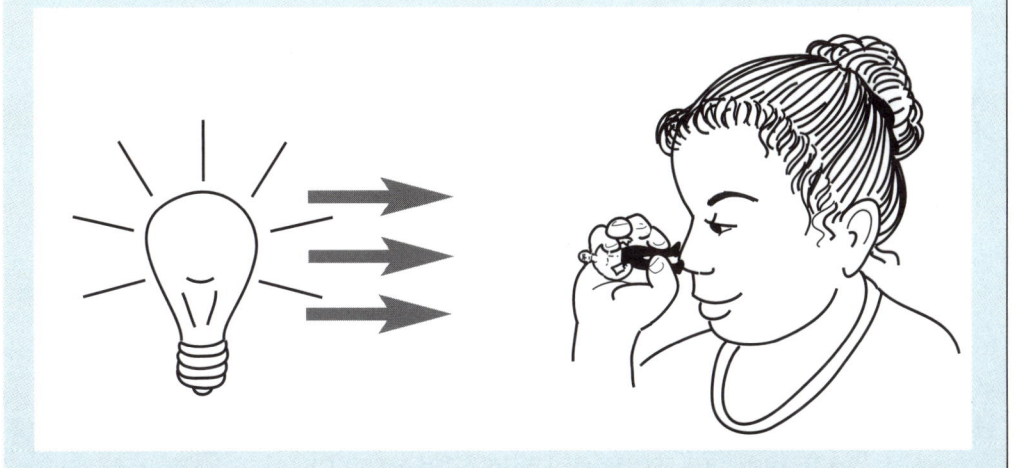

Optional Prerequisite Activities

Prerequisite Activities	Estimated Time
What Is the Shape of Earth's Orbit?	30 minutes

What Is the Shape of Earth's Orbit?

In this activity, students discover that although Earth's orbit is elliptical, that ellipse is very nearly a perfect circle. This activity can help to dispel the common misconception that seasons are caused by a variation in the distance between the Sun and Earth.

What You Need

For the class:
- ❑ a 40-cm piece of string or twine (not stretchy)
- ❑ a large, blank sheet of paper (at least 14" x 14")
- ❑ tape
- ❑ 2 pushpins or thumbtacks
- ❑ a marker
- ❑ a ruler with centimeter markings

For each pair of students:
- ❑ a 25-cm piece of string or twine (not stretchy)
- ❑ a pencil
- ❑ a blank sheet of paper
- ❑ 2 pushpins or thumbtacks
- ❑ a stack of newspaper (thick enough to stick the pins or tacks into)
- ❑ a ruler with centimeter markings

Getting Ready

1. **Prepare to demonstrate how to draw an ellipse to the class.** Tie the ends of the 40-cm piece of string together to form a loop. Attach a large piece of paper (at least 14" x 14") to a bulletin board. If you don't have a bulletin board, you may need to put a piece of cardboard or another such surface onto the wall on which to attach the paper. Read through Step #2 below and practice drawing an ellipse.

2. **Prepare a loop of string for each pair of students.** Tie the ends of the 25-cm pieces of string together to form loops. The loop should be 8 cm long when stretched flat. An easy way to do this is to stick two pushpins 8 cm apart into a thick piece of cardboard. Tie the string around the pushpins. Test the loops to make sure that the knots are tight.

374 • SPACE SCIENCE SEQUENCE 6-8   Optional: Prerequisite Activities

TEACHER CONSIDERATIONS

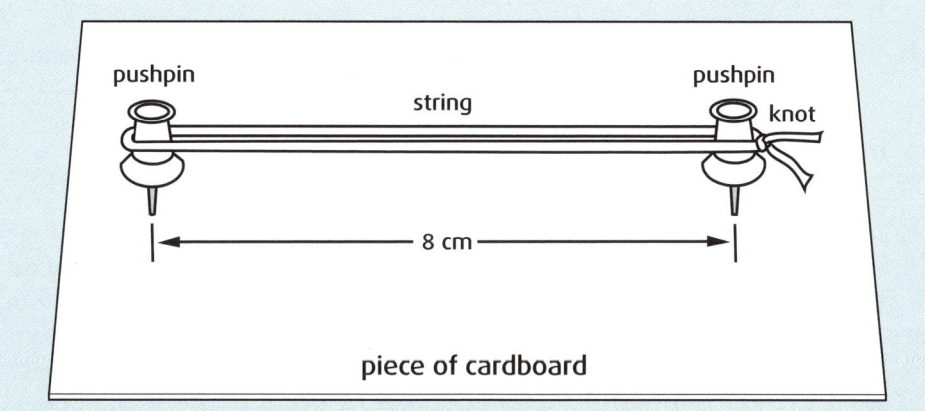

pushpin · string · pushpin · knot · 8 cm · piece of cardboard

Optional Prerequisite Activities

GO! What Is the Shape of Earth's Orbit?

1. **Explain the term *ellipse*.** Explain that an *ellipse* is an oval shape—a very precise and symmetrical oval shape. Tell students that all objects in the Solar System—including planets, comets, and asteroids—revolve around the Sun in elliptical orbits.

2. **Demonstrate how to draw an ellipse.** Show the class the following steps to draw a near-Earth asteroid's orbit:

   a. Use the marker to make two marks, 6 cm apart, on a piece of paper posted to the bulletin board.

   b. Stick a pushpin through each mark and into the bulletin board.

   c. Drape the string loop you made from a 40-cm piece of string over the pushpins.

   d. Ask for a volunteer to hold one of the pushpins steady.

   e. Hold the other pushpin steady and pull the string taut with the tip of the marker.

   f. **Draw the ellipse, keeping the string taut at all times.** While you are drawing, emphasize the importance of keeping the string taut as well as having two people working together to make sure the pushpins stay firmly in place while making the ellipse.

3. **Introduce the term *focus*.** Explain that each point where a pushpin goes in is called a *focus* of the ellipse. Mention that the plural of focus is *foci* (FOE- sigh). Point out that the orbit you drew is fairly skinny or elongated—not circular. Explain, also, that in the orbits of planets (as well as comets or asteroids), the Sun remains fixed at only one of the foci of the ellipse.

4. **Have students draw ellipses.** Divide the class into pairs and assign students to draw two orbits: one near-Earth asteroid orbit with foci separated by 5 cm and one Earth orbit with foci separated by 0.5 cm. Tell students to work cooperatively and take turns drawing—one student should help keep the pushpins steady while the other student is drawing.

5. **Comparing orbits.** After pairs have finished drawing their two orbits, ask, "Which orbit is more circular—the asteroid's or Earth's?" [Earth's.] Explain that, while it is true that Earth's orbit is slightly elliptical, it is very nearly a circular ellipse. Point out that if the Sun is always at a focus of the ellipse, and the foci are very close together, then the Sun is very close to the center of the ellipse. So, not only is Earth's orbit almost circular, the Sun is in the center of the orbit.

TEACHER CONSIDERATIONS

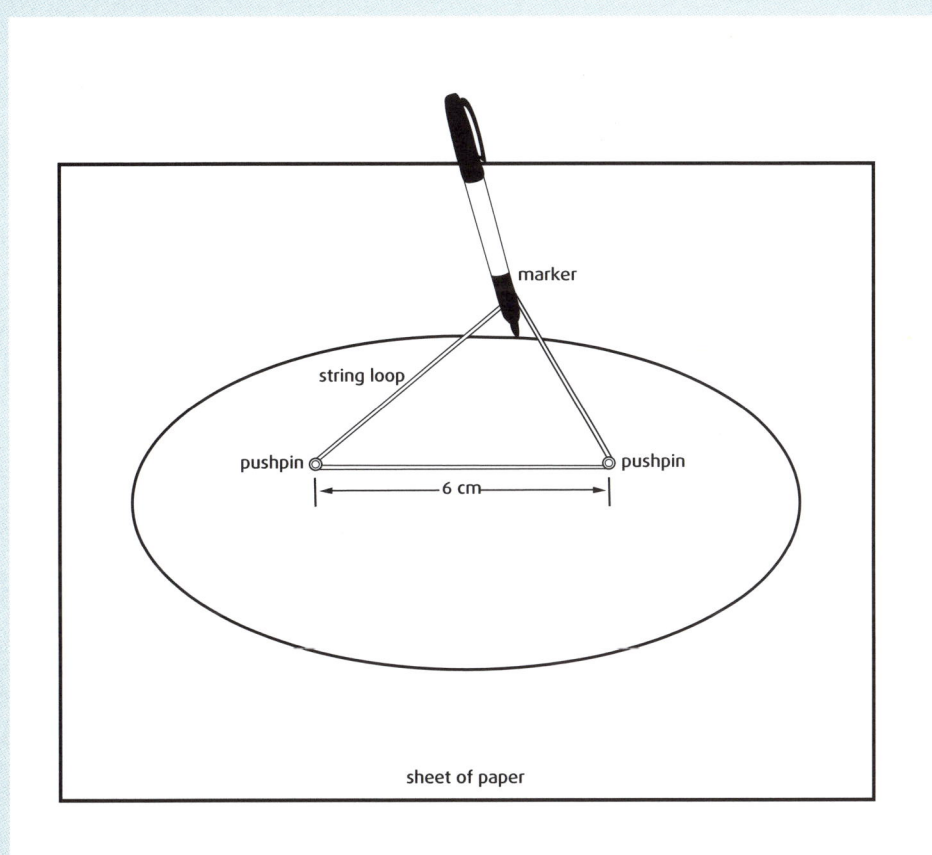

marker

string loop

pushpin   pushpin

|—6 cm—|

sheet of paper